MEN, MICROSCOPES, AND LIVING THINGS

Also by Katherine B. Shippen

I KNOW A CITY

A BRIDLE FOR PEGASUS

LIGHTFOOT

THE BRIGHT DESIGN

THE GREAT HERITAGE

NEW FOUND WORLD

MEN OF MEDICINE

MEN, MICROSCOPES, AND LIVING THINGS

by Katherine B. Shippen

ILLUSTRATED BY ANTHONY RAVIELLI

New York

THE VIKING PRESS

LITHOGRAPHED IN THE U. S. A. BY MURRAY PRINTING COMPANY

"In performing these researches so many
marvels of nature were spread before my eyes
that I experienced an internal pleasure that my
pen could not describe."

MARCELLO MALPIGHI

(1628–1694)

CONTENTS

MEN, MICROSCOPES,
AND LIVING THINGS

I. BETWEEN THE HEIGHTS
AND THE DEPTHS

HIGH on the bleak flanks of the Himalaya Mountains, where no other animal life can survive and no green thing can grow, mountain climbers have found little jumping spiders. It is thought that they feed on pollen grains blown up to those high places by the wind. Eagles and vultures soar over those lonely peaks, though they come down to lower altitudes to nest.

Life is moving at the other extreme too, in the darkness of the ocean's floor. Strange fish live there in spite of enormous pressure and glacial cold. Some of them are furnished with phosphorescence, as if they were carrying lanterns in the ocean's dark. Here too are diatoms, the microscopic plant life of the sea, and little single-celled creatures, called radiolarians, that look like lacy snowflakes.

Between these heights and depths, as the ball of the earth moves around the sun, are all the living things we know—the trees and the grass; the spiders and the bees; the ants and the grasshoppers; the birds and bright-scaled fish; the oysters and clams; the dolphins, whales, and man himself. The earth and air and sea are filled with their activity. They are feeding and growing, reproducing their kind and dying, in endless cycles. Furry animals and those with hairy hides are moving through the forests and across the plains; birds are gathering for their great migrations; mosses and lichens, ferns and fungi, are taking nourishment from the earth and air. Clams, sponges, and corals follow their various ways.

For life is movement and activity. The only real quietness is death.

Among all the various living things, man takes his place, for he is part of them. Like all the rest he must seek nourishment, must reproduce his kind, and die.

But man is different from the other living things. He is the only one who can control the environment in which he lives. And only gradually has he become aware of the life around him. Only very recently has he understood that all living things are connected with one another like a great chain of many links, and that he himself is a part of the chain.

When he learned to use fire, to domesticate animals and cultivate the fields, he had dominion over other living things. He learned early which serpents were dangerous, which vegetables could be eaten, which animals tamed for work. He learned to live in a cave and later to build himself a house. He learned to use the furs and fleece of animals to make himself garments, because nature had given him such poor protection from the cold.

Man was different from the living things around him because he used his ingenuity to sustain his life and to control his environment.

But though man dominated the things around him he did not understand them, nor did it seem at all possible to him that there was any connection between him and them. He would have been surprised if anyone had told him that he was in any way related to a jellyfish or that the substance of a lily pad was like the stuff of which his hand was made. A jellyfish was a jellyfish, and a lily pad was a lily pad, and he was a man. There were countless plants and animals that he had never even noticed, but it did not matter.

As time passed, gifted men of various races took living

things as models for designs in painting or in weaving. So in an old Egyptian papyrus you may see ducks swimming among the reeds at the edge of the Nile, or in a Persian rug a pattern of intermingled flowers. The Minoans carved animals, and painted them on the walls of their palaces more than two thousand years before Christ. Here you may see antelopes quietly feeding or startled at a sound; there fallow deer are browsing, or dogs are chasing them. The figures are carefully portrayed. The lie of the feathers on a birds' head, the teeth in a lion's mouth, the placing of the scales on the side of a fish—all these were noticed and set down. But the purpose of such work was to affirm the beauty of fish, beast, or flower, not to explain its structure. Perhaps the artist portrayed it so accurately because he could imagine nothing more perfect than its natural form.

The Greeks, with their boundless curiosity and their zest for living, were the first to be scientifically interested in living things. Hippocrates, in the seventh century before Christ, founded a school of medicine where dissections were done and a list of medicinal plants was made.

We still have a few of Hippocrates' writings; it is possible to see in them how the ancient physicians worked. One passage of his book is especially interesting, for it shows what might be called a scientific attitude toward the human body. Some people had said that certain diseases were caused by the gods, but Hippocrates wrote: "It does not matter whether you call such things divine or not. In nature all things are alike in this, that they can be traced to preceding causes. . . ."

Those early Greek scientists in Hippocrates' medical school, forever trying to seek out the causes of things, did not stop even at trying to find out the cause of life itself. All things are made of earth, air, fire, and water, they said.

But even the early Greeks did not observe nature for its own sake, but only to cure the ailments of their bodies. Aristotle was the first to watch, to try to classify, to attempt to find out how life begins, and to write down his observations. Some scientists today believe he was the greatest natural scientist of all time.

The questions that Aristotle asked have not all been answered. For a long time the books that he wrote were neglected and his work was half forgotten. Then, one after another, gifted, curious men took up the work he had begun, found errors he had made, checked facts he had established, added new facts, until gradually science attempted to explore everything in the domain of life from the highest mountains to the deepest seas. Slowly man tried not merely to dominate and use, but to understand.

II. THE FIRST BIOLOGIST

A T THE stern of a small boat off the coast of Lesbos on
the Aegean Sea, Aristotle leaned far out over the
clear, shallow water, looking down at a catfish that was
laying its eggs among the reeds. Hour after hour he
watched, holding his boat steady with a strong pole so that
it would not float away. When darkness came down over
the water so that he could no longer see, he pulled up the
pole and rowed back to the shore. In his study, by the light
of an oil lamp, he made a record of what he had seen.

"The catfish deposits its eggs in shallow water, generally
close to roots or close to reeds. The eggs are sticky and
adhere to the roots.

"The female catfish, having laid her eggs, goes away.
The male stays on, and watches over the eggs, keeping
off all other little fishes that might steal the fish or fry.
He thus continues for forty or fifty days, till the young are
sufficiently grown to escape from the other fishes themselves.

"Fishermen can tell where he is on guard, for in warding

off the little fishes he sometimes makes a rush in the water and gives utterance to a kind of muttering noise. Knowing his earnestness in parental duty, the fishermen drag into a shallow place the roots of water plants to which the eggs are attached, and there the male fish, still keeping by the young, is caught by the hook when snapping at the other fish that come by. Even if he perceive the hook, he will still keep by his charge, and will even bite the hook in pieces with his teeth."

After he had watched the breeding habits of the catfish for a long time, Aristotle began to study other things about fish.

"Fishes can produce no voice," he wrote, "for they have no lungs or windpipe, but certain of them, as the catfish in the river Achelous, emit inarticulate sounds and squeaks by a rubbing motion of their gill covers."

Again he studied the torpedo fish. "It stuns the creatures that it wants to catch, overpowering them by the force of shock in its body and feeding upon them," he observed.

And he wrote of the fish called the angler: "He stirs himself up a place where there is plenty of mud and sand and hides himself there. He has a filament projecting in front of his eyes. The filament is long and thin and hair-like and rounded at the tip. It is used as bait. The little creatures on which this fish feeds swim up to the filament, taking it for a bit of the seaweed that they eat. Then the angler raises the filament, and when the little fishes strike against it he sucks them down into his mouth."

So day after day from the stern of his small boat near the shore Aristotle watched the life of the underwater world unfold. Everyone had seen fish before, and the fishermen knew something about their habits, for this knowledge helped them to get a bigger catch. But until then no one had watched the ways of fish for the single purpose of trying to understand them. No one had reasoned, before Aristotle's time, that if he could observe and record the ways of marine animals he would have made a beginning toward understanding life itself.

Life and the ways of living creatures were for Aristotle an absorbing mystery. He wanted to understand the growth and death of an olive tree, a violet blooming on the hillside, a clam in the sand, a bee, a goat, a man.

Aristotle thought that if he observed each living thing carefully enough, and recorded what he saw, he would come closer to an understanding of life. He had great patience and extraordinary powers of observation, and besides these two essential qualities he had an imagination which made it possible for him to interpret what he saw. It is not strange that those who followed him thought it was useless to try to add anything to his knowledge.

Modern scientists might think that Aristotle worked under great disadvantages. He had no books to consult, for no books on natural history had been written. He had no scientific training, no scientific instruments, no colleagues with whom he could discuss his findings. What he did have was inexhaustible energy and enthusiasm and a love of living things. Sometimes when he wrote of his observations he drew diagrams to make his meaning clear —the first such diagrams in scientific writing. He refers to them often in his writings; but unfortunately these diagrams have been lost.

After a time Aristotle left the study of fishes and began to study mammals. He knew very well the difference between mammals and fishes. "Mammals have lungs, breathe air, and have warm blood," he said. "They bring forth their young alive. Among them are man, the horse, the seal, and also marine animals like the whale and the dolphin. . . . The dolphin has been seen asleep with his nose above water, and snoring," he wrote.

Aristotle was by no means a young man when he began his study of natural history. He had been born in the town of Stagira on the Macedonian frontier. But his father, Nicomachus, a rich physician employed by Amyntas II of Macedonia, had great ambitions for his son and had sent him to Athens at the age of seventeen. Athens then was the center of all grace and beauty, of lovely architecture, of drama and music. Here the young Aristotle was enrolled at the Academy, in whose gardens fortunate young men studied logic, poetry, and philosophy under the great teacher, Plato.

It was not long before Aristotle became distinguished
at the Academy. Plato called Aristotle's house "the house
of the reader," for he had collected a great number of
parchment scrolls there—the first true library in Europe.
Aristotle remained at the Academy for twenty years, and
at Plato's death many thought he would become its head.
But instead he crossed the Aegean to live at the court
of Hermias, the rich king of Asia Minor, and here he
married the king's sister, Pythias.

It was here on the shore of the Lesbian Gulf that he
began his biological studies. But they had been carried on
for only about five years when another change came in
Aristotle's life. Philip, king of Macedonia, asked him to
be tutor to Alexander, his son. Alexander was a boy of
thirteen then, a passionate youth who loved to tame wild
horses that no one else could tame.

Plutarch said, "For a while Alexander loved and cherished Aristotle no less than as if he had been his own
father, saying that if he had received life from the one,
the other had taught him the art of living."

But Aristotle and Alexander remained together only a
few years. Then Alexander, having inherited his father's
throne, set off on his Asian expedition, and Aristotle, after
a brief period of travel, settled down in Athens again.
Here he helped to establish a great zoological garden.

Pliny, writing in 77 A.D., said that Alexander founded
it. He wrote: "Alexander the Great, fired by the desire

to learn of the nature of animals, entrusted the prosecution of this design to Aristotle. . . . For this end he placed at his disposal some thousands of men in every part of Asia and Greece, and among them hunters, fowlers, fishers, park-keepers, herdsmen, bee-wards, as well as keepers of fish ponds and aviaries, in order that no creature might escape his notice. Through the information thus collected he [Aristotle] was able to compose some fifty volumes."

Having the direction of such a great undertaking as this, and composing "some fifty volumes," might seem enough. But Aristotle wanted to share his findings with others, and to have them help him with research. That was why he founded his great school, the Lyceum.

The Lyceum was to be a very different place from the Academy in which he had studied under Plato for so many years. Plato had discussed philosophy and poetry with his young Athenians, but the Lyceum was a scientific school. Here, Aristotle dreamed, all the knowledge that had been accumulated through the years would be organized and set down for future generations to build upon.

The school was called the Lyceum because it was situated in the grounds of the temple of Apollo Lyceus, the god who protected the flocks from attacking wolves. There was a long promenade beside the athletic field of the temple, and here the students talked with the master as they strolled up and down. In the morning Aristotle's pupils were the older men, gray-haired and full of knowledge; in the afternoon they were the young men.

What did they talk about, strolling back and forth beside the level green stretch of the athletic field?

They talked of the living principle, the essence that distinguished all living things. Aristotle called this the *psyche* or soul, meaning the principle of life.

He thought there were different kinds of psyches and that, therefore, one could distinguish between the vegetable, the animal, and the human soul. Plants have the lowest form of soul, he said. They take food from the environment around them; they grow and reproduce. Animals have these powers too, but they can also move from place to place; while men, having all the powers possessed by plants and animals, can, in addition, reason and control their actions.

Between all these living things there must be some connection, and Aristotle attempted to arrange them in a great ladder, the *scala natura,* as it was called later.

"Nature proceeds little by little from things lifeless to animal life in such a way that it is impossible to determine the exact line of demarcation, nor on which side thereof an intermediate form should lie. Thus next after lifeless things in the upward scale comes the plant. Of plants one will differ from another as to its amount of apparent vitality. In fact the whole plant-kind, whilst devoid of life as compared with animal-kind, is endowed with life as compared with other forms of matter. Indeed there is in plants a continual scale of ascent toward the animal. Thus one is at a loss to say of certain beings in the sea whether they be animal or vegetable. . . ."

So Aristotle talked with his pupils, and he set down his conclusions in book after book—a great compendium of knowledge.

Many of his observations and conclusions have been verified by later scientists; many are still under discussion. For example, there are today two main schools of biologists: the vitalists, who believe, as Aristotle did, that the functions of a living organism are due to a vital force, distinct from physical forces; and the mechanists, who regard all phenomena of nature as caused by merely mechanical forces.

For twelve years Aristotle and his scholars worked, assembling their great mass of knowledge, writing many books. They investigated the beginnings of life in the embryo. "He who sees things grow from the beginning will have the finest view of them," they said. They examined the structures of plants and wondered at the effect of the sun on them. They dissected reptiles and studied the habits of insects. "The consideration of the lowlier forms of life should not excite a childish repugnance," Aristotle told his pupils. For "in every form of life . . . there is something of Nature and Beauty."

Most of Aristotle's books have been lost, but enough of

his writings remain to establish him as probably the greatest biologist that ever lived.

And what happened to him? How did it end? Alexander
the Great died of a fever in Babylon. There was a revolution of the Greeks against Macedonian rule. Everyone who
had any connection with Alexander was suspect. They
said that Aristotle should be tried for "godlessness."

Aristotle must have known what the outcome of such a
trial would be. Perhaps he thought of the fate of Socrates,
who had also been tried for "godlessness." He left the
Lyceum and took ship for the island of Euboea. But he
lived for only about a year after that.

After Aristotle's death, when peace was restored in
Athens and the Lyceum was reopened, Theophrastus, his
pupil, became its head.

Theophrastus lived to be a very old man, and when he
died he left a will providing money to preserve a marble
bust of his master. That is why the face of the first biologist
is familiar to us after more than two thousand years.

III. PLINY'S TALL TALES

THE ROMANS, with their great empire, had a genius for government and for war and for many other things, but they had little genius for science. They were a practical people. To watch the doings of a catfish in a river bed would have seemed to them a hopeless waste of time.

It is true that Galen, who was a physician in the school of gladiators at Rome during the time of Marcus Aurelius, added some new information on how men's bodies functioned. And Dioscorides, who was a military surgeon under Marcus Aurelius, made a list of herbs that could be used in treating various ailments, and illustrated it with little drawings. But, on the whole, scientific observation came to a stop under the Romans.

This does not mean that the Romans were completely uninterested in science. In fact they were quite interested in it. But they did not want to add anything to what had already been found out or to make any new observations. They wanted to make compilations of what other people had discovered.

This was what Gaius Plinius Secundus spent his time doing—Pliny the Elder we call him now.

Pliny was born in the first century A.D., and was well educated by good private teachers in Rome. He held a military command in Germany for a long time, and afterward became a commander of the Roman fleet. But all the time he was leading his official life he managed to study and to write, not putting into his writing his own ideas or his own observations, but assembling what other men had learned. He wrote on military science, on history, on rhetoric and linguistics. But the only work that has been preserved is his work on natural history.

Pliny's *Natural History* is a staggering piece of work. It

is an encyclopedia of all the scientific knowledge that was known down to his time. It is divided into thirty-seven books which deal with the universe, with geography, anthropology, zoology, botany—including the medicinal uses of plants—and mineralogy.

He said he consulted two thousand books in making it, and talked with animal-keepers in Roman circuses and with priests who made sacrifices in the temples. The information was secondhand, and much of it untrue. But when Pliny died in 79 A.D., in the eruption of Mount Vesuvius, he had added practically nothing to man's store of knowledge. He had not even found a way to classify the facts already known.

Yet it is interesting to look through Pliny's *Natural History*, if only to smile at its vagaries.

In his book on animals he makes a list of all the animals that he has ever heard of, and since he does not know how to arrange them he puts the largest ones first and considers them most important. He describes the habits of every animal, and the mischief it can do, and when it was first exhibited in Rome. He loves marvels and puts down every strange fact that he can find.

He says they are fools who believe in sirens, in griffons, or in birds with heads of horses. But then he describes, quite seriously, men who bark like dogs, lands where the sun casts no shadow, and people with but one leg and a single foot apiece. Their feet are so enormous that when it is hot they lie on their backs and each one uses his foot as an umbrella for shade.

The elephant, since it is the biggest, he considers the most important of all animals.

"Amongst land animals the elephant is the largest and the one whose intelligence comes nearest to that of man," he says. "For he understands the language of his country, obeys commands, has a memory for training, takes delight in love and honor, and possesses a rare thing even amongst men—honesty, self-control, and a sense of justice; he also worships stars, and venerates the sun and moon. In the mountains of Mauretania it is said that herds of elephants move at new moon down to a river by the name of Amilo, ceremoniously cleanse themselves there by spraying one another with water, and after having thus paid their respects to the heavenly light return to the forests, bearing their weary calves with them. It is also said that when they are to be transported overseas, they refuse to go on board until the master of the ship has given them a promise under oath to convey them back again."

One of Pliny's ideas about animals that has persisted in some places even to this day was that every animal, every fish or insect, must in some way be useful to man. So he asks, Of what use is an ant, or what use is a viper? He never considers that each creature has its own life to live, its own independent activity, its own birth and hunger and death, without relation to the life of man.

Whatever the source, however strange or contradictory the facts, Pliny put them all down till his *Natural History* grew bigger and bigger. Its very size was impressive. People began to think the facts in it *must* be true, they had taken so long to put together. Gradually, as the Roman Empire spread and then crumbled away, Pliny's great volumes were held to be more and more important. No one questioned their authority. What Pliny had written remained the main source of man's knowledge of natural history for nearly fifteen hundred years.

IV. THE HERB-GATHERERS

TIME passed. The Roman Empire crumbled. New
kingdoms grew; new wars were fought. The parchment scrolls on which Aristotle's researches were recorded
were scattered, and most of them lost, though the Mo-
hammedan scholars in Spain and North Africa, and the
Hebrew students in Palestine, still read them. In Europe
people continued to talk of Aristotle as if he were some
kind of god, but few knew much about his work, and no
one thought of following his methods.

Pliny was much more popular. His books were copied

and recopied, his sayings quoted over and over again—for people are generally more interested in the curious than in the scientific.

And every year, through all that time that has been called the Dark Ages, soft blooms lighted up the hillsides and the meadows every spring; frogs croaked in the ponds; birds built their nests and laid their eggs. Every year the beavers built their dams and swam back and forth across the ponds with sticks to build their houses; every year the deer slept on the sunny hillsides in the daylight and roamed through the forests at night; every year the fish flashed in the rivers.

During the Middle Ages no heed was paid to the living things that were man's companions. The animals were thought to be in the devil's keeping, and the plant life was taken for granted.

There was, however, an exception to this: the herb-gatherers had to know one plant from another. No one thought much of their profession, to be sure. The practice of medicine in those days was thought not respectable; doctors and magicians were classed together. Still, if men were sick they needed cures, and herbs were the *materia medica*.

Sometimes a physician went out in search of his "simples" himself, but more often herb-gatherers ranged through the forest and meadows, collecting the various plants and roots that were on the lists of medicines, and selling them to the doctors. The monasteries sent out a great many monks on this quest too, for every religious house kept a good supply of medicinal herbs, not only for the monks themselves, but for the people of the surrounding country.

The herb-gatherers made their way through the woods, trying to identify various plants and roots in a hit-or-miss way, without any classification. People generally despised them and felt contempt for their calling. They were afraid of them too, because their trade appeared to be so close to sorcery.

Gathering herbs was by no means an easy task. It must have been exasperating and difficult to find the plants and roots on the medical lists. The herb-gatherers did, of course, have some books called herbals to help them— queer, old, leather-bound books with parchment pages on which descriptions and drawings had been copied by hand in the monasteries over and over again. They had been taken from the Greek writings of Theophrastus and Dioscorides, and the Greek translated into Latin. Each time a work was copied mistakes were made, so the new copy differed a little more from the original. Hence the herbals on which the herb-gatherers depended were very little like the originals.

The pictures of plants in these books were more altered in copying than was the text. In one drawing a strawberry plant, whose leaves characteristically appear in clusters of three, was drawn with leaves in clusters of four or even five. The runners gradually began to appear to be thorns. If the copyist had put down his brush and gone outdoors to look at the strawberry plant, he might have succeeded better, but apparently he never thought of this.

There was still another difficulty which the herb-gatherers had. Theophrastus and Dioscorides had described the plants they saw, which were of course in Greece. But in the forests of northern Europe, where the herb-gatherers worked, the plants and roots of Theophrastus and Dioscorides were not to be found. Apparently no one up to that time had realized that different plants grow in different localities.

It was a great step forward when, much later, a brand-new herbal was made, not a copy. Here for the first time the flowers of northern Europe were sketched and described. Here were the lilies of the valley that grew wild around Oberammergau, heartsease, or wild pansy, and ragged robin, which was used as part of a secret formula by the monks of Chartreuse in making their liqueur.

As time passed, other herbals began to appear. Many of them are still to be seen in libraries. They show strange notions with regard to various parts of plants, but these notions were held by the best-informed students of the day. It was thought quite universally then that the head of a plant was in its roots, that the flower served to cool its "vapors," that the pollen was the plant's excreta, and that its soul was to be found where the stem joined the roots.

It was also believed in those days that God had set a mark on every plant to show how it could be useful to men —and therefore why He had created it. So a plant with leaves spotted like the liver was thought to be good for liver complications. Large quantities of little blue-flowered hepaticas were collected on this account. Plants with heart-shaped leaves would be good for heart disease. A leaf shaped like a foot would be helpful for lameness. And so it went.

Of all the herbs collected in the Middle Ages, the mandrake was the most prized. Its long, forked root resembled the human form, and so it was inferred that this root would cure any part of the human body. It was a powerful narcotic and was used to dull pain, but, more than this, people used it in making love potions, and they thought it would increase wealth and overcome barrenness.

Perhaps because the mandrake root looked so much like a little man there were all sorts of superstitions about gathering it. Some said it would bring bad luck to him who pulled it up. Some said that it would scream when it was drawn from the ground. For these reasons careful directions were set down for gathering the mandrake root.

One herbal directed: "Thou shalt in this manner take it. When thou comest to it, then thou understandeth it by this, that it shineth at night, altogether like a lamp. When first thou seest its head, then inscribe [encircle] thou it instantly with iron, lest it fly from thee; its virtue is so mickle and so famous that it will immediately flee from an unclean man when he cometh to it; hence as we said before inscribe it with iron, and so shalt thou delve about it, as that thou touch it not with the iron, but thou shalt earnestly with an ivory staff delve the earth. And when thou seest its hands and its feet, then tie thou it up. Then take the other end and tie it to a dog's neck, so that the hound be hungry; next cast meat before him, so that he may not reach it except he jerk up the wort with him."

Later the herbal says: "Of this wort it is said that it hath so mickle might that what thing soever tuggeth it up, that it shall soon in the same manner be deceived. Therefore as soon as thou see that it be jerked up, and have possession of it, take it immediately in hand, and twist it, and wring the ooze out of its leaves into a glass ampulla."

So eager were the herb-gatherers to get mandrake roots, and so difficult and frightening were these to procure, that sometimes they tried to make other roots look like little men. One Turner, in his *Herball*, was very scornful of this practice.

"The rootes which are counterfeited and made like little pupettes and mammettes, which come to be sold in England in boxes, with heire and such forme as a man hath, are nothynge elles but folishe trifles, and not naturall. For they are so trymmed of crafty theves to mocke the poore people with all, and to rob them both of theyre wit and theyre money. I have in my tyme at diverse tymes taken up the rootes of Mandrag out of the grounds, but I never saw any such thing upon or in them as they are in and upon the pedlers' rootes that are comenly to be sold in boxes."

To the herb-gatherers moving back and forth across the swamps and through the thickets of northern Europe, every plant and every root was a blessing and a curse to man—a cure of ills, a source of wealth, a thing of fearful mystery and dread.

But as time passed, more and more men broke free from superstition and began to collect plants in order to study them. A monk in Germany left his monastery and set off on a long journey to collect material to make an herbal. There was also a rich old gentleman who employed an artist to accompany him while he went botanizing in the East. Their names are now forgotten.

But though gradually men were beginning to put aside the superstitions that had surrounded plants for so long, they had not yet found out much about them. They would have been surprised to learn that all the herbs and roots had not been created for "the delight of the healthy and the comfort and life of the sick," but were part of the world in which men and all other living things are joined.

V. HEDGEHOGS AND UNICORNS

ALTHOUGH the herb-gatherers were growing more or less familiar with plants and roots, because they were needed for medicine, much less intelligence was used with regard to animals. Deer and rabbits were shot for food, horses and dogs were tamed, and hawks were trained

·for hunting birds. A few other common animals were known, but in general a feeling of fear and mystery surrounded the wild creatures.

Sometimes, to be sure, the schoolmen discussed animals and quoted learned authorities to reinforce their arguments. The question of how many teeth were in a horse's mouth was debated with great heat in many learned circles. Solemn books were written on this subject, with references to other learned books, but no one thought to open a horse's mouth to count its teeth, for this was the age when learning looked to authority.

Progress is not made by having one learned authority quote another, and it is not strange that no original works on zoology were produced in the early Middle Ages. There was, however, one book on animals that was read everywhere, a book so curious and so widely known that it must be considered here, though it certainly cannot be said it is in any way scientific.

The book is called *Physiologus*, and no one knows who wrote it, but it probably had a number of authors. It is a collection of stories about animals. Such a book was called a bestiary. Each story has a moral attached to it, and is intended to describe the habits of the animal and also to set forth the teachings of the Church.

Physiologus was enormously popular. The stories were translated into Icelandic and Ethiopian, and they were read and recited by popes and friars, taught in the universities, and told at almost every fireside. They were copied by the monks; and every monastery had a book of them. The animals of the stories were carved in the choirs and chancels of churches and cathedrals. There was no one in Europe in the Middle Ages who did not know *Physiologus.*

It must be admitted that these animals had lively personalities. Some of them were familiar ones that everybody had seen or knew about; some were more exotic—creatures that lived in distant lands and so were seldom seen. No one had ever met with some of them, but everyone believed that they existed. Just as the herbalists thought that every plant that grew held either a blessing or an evil omen for mankind, so it was with the animals, according to this book.

So *Physiologus* says of the hedgehog, an animal that must have been fairly familiar to the peasants of northern Europe:

". . . he is a small beast shaped like a ball entirely set round with prickles. He procures his nourishment in this way: he goes to a vine, reaches down to the clusters, tears off the grapes, and casts them on the ground. Then he throws himself down, and the grapes fasten onto his prickles, and he brings them home to his children, and leaves the clusters empty on the vine.

"The hole in which the Hedgehog lives is provided with two openings and is bored with air holes, and, when the

north wind begins to blow, he stops the opening which
is turned to the north wind, but when the south wind
blows he stops the opening which is turned to the south
wind and opens the north hole which he before had
stopped."

Stories are told of the fox, which "is a very crafty animal. . . . He casts himself on his back, and holds his breath
and swells up his body completely, so that he appears
dead. The birds believe that he is really dead and they fly
down to him in order to eat him up; but he springs up and
catches them and eats them up."

And of the whale *Physiologus* says: "There is a great
monster in the sea called the Whale. He has two attributes.
His first attribute is this: when he is hungry, he opens wide
his jaws, and therefrom streams a very sweet savor. And
all the little fishes gather themselves in heaps and shoals
round the whale's mouth, and it laps them all up, but the
big and full-grown fish keep away from him. . . .

"The other attribute of the Whale is as follows. The
monster is very large, just like an island. Now the sailors
in their ignorance moor their boat to him as to the shore of
an island. They make a fire thereon to cook their meal.
And when the monster feels the heat, then he dives down
into the depths of the sea, and carries the boat with him,
man and mouse."

Here is the woodpecker: "a gay-colored bird," who "gets
up into the trees and pecks at them with his beak, and

listens with his ear"; the peacock: "He is beautiful of color and lordly in plumage. When he passes by, he looks at himself and rejoices much over himself. He shakes himself, turns a somersault and looks proudly around. . . ."

Later, if you turn the pages, you will read about the eagle, who "when he is aging, his flight grows heavy and his eyesight dim. What does he now do? He seeks first a pure spring of water, and flies aloft to the ether of the sun, and burns off his old feathers and loosens the film over his eyes, and flees down to the spring, and therein dives three times under, and becomes young again. . . ."

And there is the snake. "When it goes to the stream to drink, it carries not its poison with it but leaves it behind in its hole. . . ."

And the less familiar lion, who, when it is pursued by the hunter, brushes away its tracks behind it with its tail; and the tiger, who rolls its young before it inside a glass ball.

Of all the descriptions of animals in *Physiologus* the one that might have disturbed Aristotle most was that of the sea urchin, for he knew the sea creatures well. *Physiologus* says this of the sea urchin:

"That which happens in the sea is beyond all speech and understanding. I have heard from one who lives on the coast that the sea urchin is a little and contemptible beast which lives in the sea and which tells the sailor whether the waves will be calm or rough. For this urchin seeks a rock, whereon he hangs and clings, and he fastens himself to it as to an anchor, so that the waves, though they toss him here and there and up and down, cannot tear him away. And this he does as though he were minded to point out beforehand the oncoming of the storm, the tumult of which is already in his mind. So soon as the sailors see him they know by this sign that danger threatens them from the violence of the wind. There is no Chaldean, no mathematician, who can read in the courses of the stars what the movements of the winds will be. . . . Who has taught this urchin, this stupid little beast—who but the Lord Himself?"

It was not hard for the men who read these descriptions of familiar or of little-known animals to take a step farther and believe in animals which no one had ever seen. So *Physiologus* describes the ant-lion, with the head of a lion and the body of an enormous ant. It always starved to death because the head wanted to eat meat and the body wanted to be fed grass. And there was the cockatrice, a deadly little serpent with the head of a cock and the body of a snake. One had but to see it to die, and the only way to defend oneself against it was to sew mirrors to one's garments so that it might see its own image first.

Later he tells of the phoenix, the Arabian bird which at the end of a certain number of years made its nest of spices, sang a melodious dirge, flapped its wings to set fire to the pile, burned itself to ashes, and came forth to a new life.

There were also the griffon, the dragon, and the winged horse, and, most popular of all, the unicorn. The unicorn was a beautiful creature, wild and shy and very fleet of foot. He was pure white, *Physiologus* said, but on his forehead he bore a single horn, one and a half cubits (about two feet) in length, colored red, black, and white. A drinking cup made of this horn would protect you against poison.

For many centuries in Europe people believed in these unseen animals quite as faithfully as in the wild creatures they had seen. There was nothing extraordinary about this. After all, there were so many things in the world then that man had not explored.

At least that was true for the great majority of people. There were, of course, a few who wanted proved facts. One of those was Frederick II of Hohenstaufen, who was Holy Roman emperor in the thirteenth century. Half-Oriental in his habits and in his way of thinking, he gathered a group of learned men from both East and West about him at his court. He established a school of medicine at Salerno, where for the first time since Alexandrian days human bodies were dissected. He had the writings of Aristotle translated from Greek to Latin, and wrote a book on falconry in which he described the anatomy and habits of birds from actual observation. All these things were efforts at scientific method, and bold ventures in his day. But at Frederick II's death they were ignored and forgotten, for his work was not in accord with the temper of his times.

There were other men here and there who also made efforts at original work. Albertus Magnus, in the thirteenth century, spent his life in editing the writings of Aristotle. And Roger Bacon tried doing actual scientific experiments, but he was imprisoned, for people thought he was dabbling in magic.

The great mass of the people continued to believe in the stories of hedgehogs and unicorns that were written in *Physiologus*—not knowing that already the winds of change were blowing.

VI. VESALIUS AND HARVEY
USE THEIR EYES

SLOWLY the world moved on. During the fifteenth and sixteenth centuries the peoples of Europe awakened as if from a dream. It was the time of the Renaissance. New trade routes had been started toward the East, new markets established, new cities built. Mariners, their little ships equipped with compasses, sailed out across unknown seas, rounded the coast of Africa, crossed the ocean to the Americas; while the telescope set others exploring the limitless skies.

Now, as if to help in spreading news of great adventures, the printing press was made, and paper was imported in quantity from Egypt; it was no longer necessary to copy manuscripts laboriously by hand on expensive parchment.

Now people began to investigate what before had been hidden. They stared at a Greek statue dug from the earth and realized the vitality of the ancient artists. With the help of Arab or Hebrew scholars they read a Greek manuscript, not translated and marred by frequent copying, but

49

in the original. They read it freshly, as it had first been written, and the classics of antiquity were reborn for them.

You can still see evidence of the vitality of the thought of that time in the work of the painters, in the affectionate and careful observation of flower and leaf, of bird and beast and man. Botticelli painted thirty different kinds of wild flowers in his picture "Spring." Michelangelo, lying on his scaffold in the Sistine Chapel, painted the strong, graceful bodies of men and women in the Bible stories he illustrated. Albrecht Dürer, in Germany, made a woodcut of a rhinoceros, modeling his work on a drawing of such an animal sent by a friend from Portugal. And Leonardo da Vinci filled his notebooks with sketches of birds' wings and of bones and joints, as if he could not see enough of them or ever tire of recording what he saw.

Not only was Leonardo an artist, but he was one of the world's great scientists. However, since the time of the Greeks there had been few other real scientists in Europe. Then Andreas Vesalius and William Harvey were born.

Neither Vesalius nor Harvey set out to do anything at all revolutionary. Both men simply used their eyes and set down what they had seen rather than what tradition had taught them.

As it happened, both men were chiefly interested in the human body. Vesalius, the Belgian, described its bones and muscles. Harvey, the Elizabethan Englishman, tried to understand how it functioned. The two men never saw each other, for Vesalius died fourteen years before William Harvey was born.

Andreas Vesalius came from Brussels. His ancestors for many generations had been doctors, so perhaps it was natural that since boyhood he had been interested in the bodies of both animals and men. It must have been a great satisfaction when he himself was sent to the University of Louvain, and later to Paris, to study medicine.

But he had not been at the University of Paris long before he grew restless and left, having decided that he could work as well at home. Soon he was collecting bones at the places of public executions, and dissecting animals; and before long he had succeeded in putting a whole human skeleton together. Gradually he gained a great reputation among physicians and scholars, so that they came from miles around to watch his dissecting operations.

He moved on to Venice; and then he received an appointment as professor at the University of Padua. It was a great thing for a young man to teach at the University of Padua in those days, for that was the scientific center of Europe. Students from everywhere, in plumed hats and flowing capes, went there to study. Sometimes Vesalius had as many as five hundred students at his demonstrations.

The old three-storied building where he taught may still be seen, its lecture rooms on the upper stories and a row of little shops on the ground floor. Over the arch of the great front door you may still read: *Gymnasium omnium disciplinarum*—"The University of All Departments of Learning." Above this is carved the great seal of the city of Padua and the words: "Enter in such mood that you daily come out wiser."

According to the usual practice of that time, Vesalius read his lectures to the students in Latin, quoting from the Greek authority for his statements. Beside him at his table a surgeon-barber acted as demonstrator, pointing out the various parts of the human or animal body under discussion. The assistant used a crude knife, for new dissecting instruments had not been invented.

But since Vesalius was of an impatient disposition, it was not long before he had thrust the demonstrator aside and was demonstrating his lectures for himself.

It was the custom then for the students to elect their own professors, and since Vesalius was very popular he was chosen to lecture at Padua for five successive years. At the end of this time, in 1542, while he was still only twenty-eight years old, he published a book to sum up the results of his lectures and demonstrations. It was called *The Fabric of the Human Body*, and it was dedicated to Emperor Charles V, the greatest monarch of his time.

Vesalius decided to illustrate his book with woodcuts, and he chose one of Titian's most gifted pupils, Jan Stephen von Calcar, to make the illustrations for him.

They were so beautifully executed that some people thought Titian himself had made them.

Vesalius regarded the human body of which he wrote as a work of art, and thought that God Himself was the Great Artist. He described the overlapping muscles of a living man, and had them drawn not in the form of diagrams but as if one could see them through the skin. In all the years that have passed since Vesalius' time, no one has drawn living muscles so beautifully as they are drawn in this book; anatomists still go back to it to learn from these drawings.

The bones and joints are also shown, starting with the skull, which Vesalius measured and compared with the skulls of other animals; and these drawings also have singular beauty and accuracy.

The whole work is done with sincerity and care. But this very carefulness brought trouble to its author, not only from the Church but from other physicians. For Vesalius' conclusions were not in accordance with tradition. The physicians objected because he showed that in the human body the lower jaw is but a single bone, not divided as the Greeks had taught. They were also indignant because he showed that the breastbone had three parts and not eight. What caused him special difficulty was the thighbone. He stated that in humans it was straight, not curved as in a dog.

His old teacher, Sylvius, was furious at this statement.

Vesalius' ideas were newfangled and dangerous, he said. Of course the Greeks were right. Men had undoubtedly changed their thighbones by foolish practices; wearing tight trousers had probably straightened out their natural curves!

The theologians were even more vehement against Vesalius than were the physicians. It was a commonly accepted idea that a man had one less rib on one side than on the other, since Eve had been fashioned out of one of Adam's ribs. And it was also believed that every man had what was called a "resurrection bone," around which his new body was formed on the resurrection day. But Vesalius could give no account of either the missing rib or the resurrection bone.

Yet though his eyes told him that the facts he had put in his book were true, Vesalius did not want to break with the old teachings or to disturb the pattern of thought that men had held so long. He was a devout man. The fabric of the human body was a beautiful thing to him, fashioned by God, but he could not force himself to say he had seen anything he had not seen.

Vesalius' work on the human body was so distinguished that he has been called one of the greatest scientists of modern times, but he was too radical for his own age. He was forced to resign his post at Padua, and moved back to Venice, and then to Jerusalem. No one knows what finally happened to him.

William Harvey, the Englishman who followed Vesalius, sympathized completely with his point of view. Both were conservatives, not wanting to upset the old established ways. But something in them both made them use their eyes and set down what they had seen. Whereas Vesalius had described the human body's structure so beautifully, Harvey wanted to show how it functioned.

There is no way of knowing how Harvey became interested in the operation of heart, lung, and digestive tract. Perhaps he did not know himself. He was born in Folkestone in England; his father was mayor of the town. Since his father was a prosperous man, the boy was given a good education—an advantage that was denied to poor boys then.

He went to school in Canterbury and afterward was sent up to Cambridge. And in due course he too traveled to Padua, not to teach but to study. He wanted to study medicine.

At Padua he sat with other students in a small, candle-lit amphitheater and looked down at an aged professor named Fabricius, who lectured on the valves of the veins. It was not long before young Harvey made friends with Fabricius, who taught him all he knew. Most of this he had to unlearn later, for Fabricius' views were altogether wrong. He held that the blood was manufactured from food taken into the body, that it lay in veins and hollow nerves, as in irrigation ditches, until it gradually evaporated like water in a field.

Harvey studied at Padua for some time and then went back to England to receive his degree as Doctor of Medicine. That was in the year 1602. He received an appointment as lecturer at the College of Physicians in London, and it was then that his great discovery was made.

There are two portraits of William Harvey which may still be seen. One hangs in the National Portrait Gallery in London, the other in the College of Physicians. In both pictures you may see his round face, his small, round, black eyes—which even in a picture are full of spirit—the hair worn rather long and straggling down on his round white collar. But pictures cannot give a sense of his quick nervous speech, his gesturing hands, or the temper that often flared up. There are memoirs of his friends and students that tell of these.

Yet though his temper was volatile, he was very careful and deliberate and slow in his work. He would make no statement until he had tested his facts again and again. He would not allow his great book, *On the Circulation of the Blood,* to be published until after he was fifty, though he had established his theory long before that time.

We speak of it today as a great book, though it is only seventy-two pages long. It was written, of course, in Latin, and very poorly printed; but that did not matter. Neither did its rather forbidding title make any difference. It was called *Essay on the Motion of the Heart and the Blood.* People since then have spoken of the book as *On the Circulation of the Blood.*

Harvey starts his book by explaining the old theories. According to these, food was converted in the liver into blood, and this passed through the veins partly to the heart—in order to receive the *spiritus vitalis,* as the vital spirit was called—and partly into the body.

Then he explains that he studied forty different kinds of animals to see whether this was what actually took place. Among them were worms, insects, crustaceans and fish, and finally the hearts of men.

After this he tells how he examined the human heart very carefully. It must be a hollow vessel, he thinks. He notices how the blood passes from the right auricle to the right ventricle and so into the pulmonary vein, with little valves to prevent its flowing in the wrong direction. Then he points out how it flows in a similar manner on the left side.

And then he begins to calculate. If the pulse beats 72 times a minute, in an hour 640 ounces of blood would be forced into the ventricle. That would be 8640 ounces in an hour, he estimates, or 540 pounds. That would be three times the weight of a man!

Thinking on this extraordinary computation, checking it over, wondering whether he could have made an error, a thought strikes him. "I began to think whether there might not be a *movement, as it were, in a circle. . . ."*

And again he says: "All things, both argument and ocular demonstration, thus confirm that the blood passes through lungs and heart by force of the ventricles and is driven thence and sent forth to all parts of the body. There it makes its way into the veins and pores of the flesh. It flows by the veins everywhere from the circumference to the center, from the lesser to the greater veins. By them it is discharged into the vena cava and finally into the right auricle of the heart. The blood is carried in one direction by the arteries, in the other by the veins, in so great a quantity that it cannot possibly be supplied all at once from the food that is taken into the body. It is therefore necessary to conclude *the blood of animals is impelled in a circle,* and is in a state of ceaseless movement. It must be, moreover, that this circulation is the act or function of the heart, which performs this act or function through its vessels."

But this was not enough. He wanted to prove his theory. So he tied a tight cord around his arm and showed how the veins swelled below the ligature. And he severed a vein and an artery and showed how they bled differently.

Finally he stated his conclusions. The arteries carry the blood from the heart out into the body. There it is passed into the ramifications of the veins, and flows from these into the principal vein and so back into the heart.

He could not explain exactly how the veins and arteries were connected. The microscope had not yet been invented, and no one knew of the capillary system.

The circulation of the blood in the body, which Harvey described, was a new conception—one that was contrary to the teachings of all former ages. He was the first man to explain this bodily process. Yet he took little credit for his brilliant theory. He thought that Aristotle had perhaps described the same process, but he could not find where the Greek biologist had written it down.

Harvey's findings were accepted without much hesitation. That is perhaps proof of how fast men's thoughts were changing. Even in his own lifetime physicians took the circulation of the blood as a matter of course. He was never criticized as Vesalius had been only a few years before. Almost unintentionally both men had used their eyes for seeing and had pushed aside the practice of relying on authority. In the years ahead, this was to be a common practice.

VII. "THE UNDERSTANDING
MUST BE STRETCHED"

F RANCIS BACON has been called "the greatest, wisest, meanest of mankind." With his wide-brimmed hat, starched ruff, and pointed beard, he was a brilliant member of Queen Elizabeth's Learned Council and a persuasive orator in Parliament. But he was sentenced to the

Tower of London because of some financial irregularities and was forced to spend the latter part of his life in retirement.

From our point of view this enforced retirement was not a bad thing, for it gave him leisure to write his great and influential book, the *Novum Organum*. It has been said that this book was written "with a magic pen."

Francis Bacon was what was then called an "amateur," one who loved learning. He was a philosopher and a scientist, and he thought, as did everyone else at that time, that science and philosophy were the same thing.

In the *Novum Organum* he wrote that no one could arrive at scientific truth by following blind tradition. The only way to understand a thing, he said, was to collect all the facts connected with it and let them pass through your brain as through a kind of mill. Scientific work for him was an enormous, patient work of collecting. Men must stretch their capacities, he said, to take in all the astonishing facts that lie around them. They had already invented the telescope and could begin to explore the skies; the compass helped their little ships to sail across unknown waters. They were beginning experiments with electricity. The world that they knew was filled with unexplained facts; that was why the scientists must stretch their capacities to take them in.

Bacon wrote: "The universe is not to be narrowed down to the limits of the understanding, which has been man's practice up to now, but the understanding must be stretched to take in the image of the universe as it is discovered."

Perhaps in writing this, Francis Bacon was merely giving voice to the spirit of his time, for here and there, everywhere through Europe in the sixteenth century, the scientists were at work. Most of them had no special training and did not hope to gain any practical benefit from their work. They were following their scientific studies merely for the sake of understanding the world that lay around them.

Often it must have seemed to them that they could make more progress if they could exchange their ideas with others who understood their problems. But roads were bad and traveling hard in those days, and there was no dependable mail service. So most of the scientific workers had to get on as best they could alone.

However, certain rich men who were interested in scientific discovery became patrons of science. Sometimes they invited several scientists to come and stay at their houses so that they could talk together. Sometimes they encouraged them to write long letters about their work, and had these copied and sent around to a large circle of interested people, or read to interested groups.

One of these patrons of science was William Gilbert, Queen Elizabeth's physician, who was himself an experimenter in electricity. Nicholas Fabri de Peiresc, a very learned man of France, was another. He seemed to know every scientist in Europe. People said his enthusiasm for finding out nature's ways had no limit.

A Minorite friar who lived in a cell of a monastery near Paris was also a patron of science. His name was Marin Marenne. Marenne, a very skillful writer who knew many languages, translated scientific treatises so that scholars of many nationalities could study them. Learned men from all over Europe came to Marenne's cell. Among them was René Descartes, the famed French philosopher, and Jean Baptiste Colbert, who was later Minister of Finance under Louis XIV. And there were many others. The little group formed one of the first learned societies in Europe.

Gradually the number of such groups or learned societies grew. After a while, whenever a scientific discovery was made it was reported to one or another of them, and scientists counted it a great honor to be invited to come to address the members. One of the most important of these societies was the Royal Society of London.

Before long the societies began to publish their proceedings, and scientific journals were printed and sent to the members. Such journals started in the seventeenth century, when Denys de Sallo employed a staff of men to copy passages of what he thought the most remarkable scientific writings. When the French Academy of Sciences was started De Sallo suggested that it take over this work; and this was done.

For a long time a man named Henry Oldenburg was secretary of the Royal Society in London. He was very enthusiastic about having the Society publish a scientific journal. He wrote:

"Whereas there is nothing more necessary for the improvement of philosophical matters than the communicating to such as apply their studies that way such things as are discovered by others; it is therefore fit to employ the press to gratifie those whose delight in profitable discoveries doth entitle them to knowledge of what this kingdom or other parts of the world do afford, as well as of the progress of the studies, labours, and attempts of the curious and learned in things of this kind. Such productions being clearly and truly communicated, desires after solid and usefull knowledge may be further entertained, ingenious endeavors and undertakings cherished, and those conversant in such matters encouraged to search out new things, impart their knowledge to one another, and contribute to the grand design of improving natural knowledge."

So before the end of the seventeenth century the scientific societies were flourishing, and investigators were reading the scientific journals avidly. But another movement helped men in their "ingenious endeavors and undertakings." This was the establishment of scientific museums. The first of these was founded by the Royal Society of London. Back in the third century B. C. the Museum of Alexandria—which was a famous center of learning—had included a school and a library. But although this new museum which the Royal Society was founding included a scientific library, it was mainly intended to house specimens on which the scientist could work. It was to have carefully collected and prepared plants, bones, dried fish, shells, and such ánimals as its curators, or caretakers, wanted to preserve.

Preserving the specimens was difficult. And this was especially true of the animal specimens. For animals lost their shapes and colors when they were dried, so that it was impossible to make satisfactory studies of them. To meet this difficulty, the eminent Irish scientist Robert Boyle, who was one of the first members of the Royal Society and who had done distinguished work in chemistry, suggested that specimens might be preserved in alcohol. Since then every biological student has been able to see specimens so preserved.

The specimens preserved in alcohol were usually kept in glass containers, and the early glass was of such poor quality that it was difficult to see through it. But in the last quarter of the seventeenth century a new kind of glass was made. It was a heavy, brilliant, crystal-like substance made of lead potash and sand. Since powdered flints were used to make the lead potash, it was generally called flint glass, or lead glass.

So, in the rooms of the Royal Society, biological specimens preserved in alcohol and contained in glass vessels soon multiplied in number. And these have been part of the equipment of biological laboratories ever since.

Since alcohol and flint glass were both rather expensive, another device for preserving animals was soon discovered. This was by the injection of certain preservative substances.

Soon the museum which the Royal Society had established was copied in other places. France, Germany, Holland, Italy, Switzerland—all had their museums where shelves bore rows of glass vessels containing specimens preserved in alcohol; where birds and butterflies and insects were preserved, and dried plants, carefully mounted, lay ready for the scholar's penetrating eye.

At Versailles, through the bounty of Louis XIV, one such museum was organized. An old French engraving of 1671 shows a picture of it. The Grand Monarch, in plumed hat and silken hose, stands with Colbert and the other French savants, their specimens around them. Hanging on the wall are the skeletons of a man, a stag, an antelope, and a lion. On a shelf are glass containers, presumably holding specimens preserved in alcohol. In the right-hand corner is a stuffed civet cat. And there are numerous other objects that may be useful to these gentlemen in their search for the understanding of natural phenomena. On a table just before the king is a microscope. He must be talking to Colbert about it. His hand in its great silken cuff is pointing to it.

VIII. "SO MANY MARVELS . . ."

THE WORLD was stirred by great events in the seventeenth century. It was then that the English ventured to plant their colonies at Jamestown and at Plymouth, that Champlain built the first French *"habitation"* in North America, and Henry Morgan, the pirate, plundered Panama. In the seventeenth century the King of England was deposed and executed, but the Stuart kings were put back on the English throne after Oliver Cromwell died. The planted fields of Germany were laid waste by marching soldiers in the Thirty Years' War, and Louis XIV ruled in splendor at Versailles.

Many other events might be added to this list, and all were important. All changed the world's history and altered the lives of men. In science, one of the most important occurrences—an occurrence of far-reaching influence—was the microscope's coming into common use among scientific men.

The microscope gave men new power. Now they could see a whole host of things that had been hidden. Now,

69

looking down in wonder through their lenses, they could enter into an infinitely fascinating, minute, and hitherto unknown world.

It has been said that a Dutch spectacles-maker named Zacharias Janssen made the first compound microscope in about 1590, but this is by no means sure. Some people claim that Galileo, who fashioned the first astronomical telescope, also ground the lens of the first microscope—but no one can prove that either.

Whoever first invented them, these microscopes were wonderful things. Some of them had only single lenses, some had double lenses with a tube between them. The sights they uncovered were a marvel to see—a whole world with its own beauties, a world totally unlike the world a man could see with his own eyes. A fly's eye through the microscope was not a brown speck but a little glass dome made up of many disks fastened together. A drop of milk was a mass of silvery globules; a crumb of bread was a rough country of branching columns; and a bit of mold was a garden full of graceful plants. It is no wonder that almost every scientist in the seventeenth century wanted to own a microscope if he could.

Signor Marcello Malpighi, professor at the medical school at Pisa in Italy, wanted very much to get a microscope. He was sure that if this instrument was all that it was said to be it would be extremely useful to him. For Signor Malpighi was lecturing to his students on the organs of the human body, and there was still so much about the human body that he did not know. There was the question of how the lungs were made. Most people thought they were masses of flesh and blood infiltrated with air. The professor doubted if that were true, but he had no way of proving the truth one way or the other.

And then there was William Harvey's theory of the circulation of the blood. The theory had great acclaim in Europe, but no one could say how the blood passed from the arteries into the veins.

Perhaps, thought Signor Malpighi, if I could examine some small animal, like a frog, under the microscope, I might make some discoveries. What is true of a frog might also be true of a human being.

Therefore he sent for a microscope. The microscope arrived in due course. He set it up on his table, and prepared a frog to study beneath its lens. Signor Malpighi was thirty-three years old then; it was the year 1661.

It is easy to imagine the quiet room; the pale, bearded face poised above the microscope's tube; the dissected frog lying quiet; the hand with a pencil, ready to sketch what the eye should see.

"It is as I thought," Signor Malpighi must have murmured to himself.

There, under the lens, he saw the frog's lung. It was sufficiently transparent to reveal a network of fibers. He looked more closely. He saw air cells enclosed by folds of lining membrane and subdivided by smaller folds. Upon the edges of all the folds ran little blood vessels. The frog's heart was still beating, and he could see the bloodstream coursing in finer and finer hairlike vessels as it passed from artery to vein through a closed network.

After many days' study Malpighi still did not understand the relation of the air to the blood in the lung, but he had found the capillary network between arteries and veins.

He turned his lens on other animals. Finally he saw the tiny capillaries connecting arteries and veins in the human body. Then he knew he had completed what William Harvey had begun. His microscope had made it possible to trace the complete circuit of the blood in the human body.

Now he turned his lens to the study of other parts of the body, and he studied the liver, the spleen, the skin. His fame was spreading through Europe fast, though he was a gentle, modest man and lived quietly because of fragile health.

About six years after he had started his work with the microscope, he received a letter from Henry Oldenburg, secretary of the Royal Society in London. Would he enter into correspondence with the Society? the letter asked. Malpighi responded gladly, and the next year he was made a Fellow of the Royal Society—a very great honor indeed.

Soon Henry Oldenburg was asking whether Malpighi would make a special study for the Society. He suggested

as a possible topic the anatomy of the silkworm. The microscope which Malpighi handled so cleverly was well
adapted to the study of insects, which were then so little
understood. Malpighi started the study at once, and
worked so hard that his eyes became red and swollen and
he developed a fever.

"Nevertheless," he wrote, "in performing these researches so many marvels of nature were spread before
my eyes that I experienced an internal pleasure which my
pen could not describe."

Two years later his study of the silkworm was ready—
a set of drawings in pencil and red chalk, with every intri-
cate, beautiful detail that he had so marveled at carefully
set down. It was the first demonstration of the delicate
design of an insect's body, and the council of the Royal
Society was so pleased with it that they ordered "that the
History of the Silk Worm, by Signor Malpighi, dedicated
to the Royal Society, be printed by the printers of the
same."

It was after this that Malpighi sent them his portrait.
It hangs in the rooms of the Royal Society in London still.

Now Malpighi began to peer through his microscope at
other things. It is said that he walked through the garden
of his friend the Viscount Ruffo, saw a broken branch of
a chestnut tree, took it home, and began to study the
structure of wood.

He prepared a treatise for the Royal Society on the

anatomy of plants, and sought to understand how life developed by opening hens' eggs each day to study beneath his lens the growth of the chicks inside.

He worked incessantly for thirty years. He moved from Pisa back to Bologna, from Bologna to Messina, and then to Rome. And always, carefully packed, he must have taken his microscope with him.

As the years passed, many of his works were published, but there were many he had not shown to anyone, and these were all lost in a fire. A friend, Dr. Tancred Robinson, wrote on April 18, 1684, that he had witnessed their destruction.

"I had several conferences with [Signor] Malpighi at Bononia. . . . He honored me with two visits at my inn. . . . Just as I left Bononia, I had a lamentable spectacle of Malpighi's house all in flames, occasioned by the negligence of his old wife. All his pictures, furniture, books, and manuscripts were burned. I saw him in the very heat of the calamity, and methought I had never beheld so much Christian patience and philosophy in any man before; for he comforted his wife, and condoled nothing but the loss of his papers. . . ."

Malpighi died not long after that. The night before his death he dictated a short account of the ear of an eagle, and signed it with his own hand.

Although so much of his work had been destroyed in the fire, what remained established his reputation as a very great scientist. He had demonstrated what could be accomplished by looking through a lens at things too delicate and minute to be studied otherwise.

In Holland not long after this two other men were turning their lenses on other aspects of life. They were Jan Jacob Swammerdam and Anton van Leeuwenhoek.

Jan Swammerdam was a very different man from the Italian, Malpighi. Where Malpighi had been gentle, patient, and sweet-tempered, Swammerdam was possessed of an irascible temper, and from earliest youth quarreled continually with those around him. He was restless, suspicious, sharp-tongued. All this can be seen in the portrait of him that Rembrandt painted.

His father was a rich apothecary who owned vessels that sailed to many parts of the world; and he had collected a large and rather famous museum of natural objects and strange creatures that fascinated the young Swammerdam. Much of his time in the years when he was growing up was spent in studying the creatures in his father's museum.

There is a story that the Duke of Tuscany, on a visit to Amsterdam, went to see the nature museum the Swammerdams had assembled. Young Swammerdam, wanting to impress the duke, took a delicate instrument and slit open a caterpillar that was ready to pass into the pupal stage. From it he drew forth the butterfly with wings, legs, and proboscis packed up in the larval skin. The duke was so impressed that he offered to buy the insect collection for twelve thousand florins, and he wanted young Swammerdam to go back to Florence with him in his retinue. Swammerdam refused to go. He preferred to stay in Amsterdam with the things in the museum.

His father, however, kept trying to get him to take up a profession. Would he be a priest? He would not even consider such a thing. Would he study medicine, then?

He did study medicine finally. In 1667 he took his M. D. degree at the University of Leyden. At the university he used a microscope. He was fascinated by it. Looking through his lens, he was first to distinguish the red corpuscles of the blood—a very important discovery for a young man to make.

After he left the university, his father wanted him to go into practice. But young Swammerdam cared for nothing but making researches with his microscope—his "flea glass," his father called it.

So he argued and quarreled with his father, and it is hard to know what might have come of it if he had not suddenly been stricken with a severe case of malaria. It was necessary for him to be sent to the country to recuperate.

It was early summer. The fields were alive with bees, crickets, and grasshoppers. And Swammerdam had brought his microscope with him. What more natural than

that he should rise every morning as soon as it was light
and go out into the fields to study insects?

He did not wear a hat because he thought it might in-
terfere with the light; the sweat poured down his face as
he worked. At night he returned to his room and made
drawings of what he had observed. He spent a whole
month in examining the intestines of bees. He then went
on to other insects and their organs.

At the end of his stay in the country he was much sicker
than he had been when he went. His eyes were so weak-
ened that he could hardly use them in the afternoons. But
his work on insects was a great masterpiece.

Now he could point with authority to the position of the
queen bee in the hive. He knew that the drones were
males and the workers neuters. He had a good idea of the
many-faceted eye of the bee, and he knew how its sting
worked.

He studied many other insects besides bees. He discovered the chitin, the horny substance which serves an
insect as a kind of outer skeleton, and he learned all about
the metamorphoses of insects.

What impressed people about Swammerdam's work
was its extreme fineness. His friend Dr. Boerhaave, who
collected his writings after his death and published them
under the title *The Bible of Nature*, marveled at the pre-
cision of Swammerdam's instruments. He wrote:

"His microscopes were of various sizes and curvatures,

his microscopical glasses being of various diameters and focuses, and from the least to the greatest, the best that could be procured, in regard to the exactness of the workmanship and the transparency of the substance.

"But the constructing of very fine scissors, and giving them an extreme sharpness, seems to have been his chief secret. These he made use of to cut very minute objects, because they dissected them equably, whereas knives and lancets, let them be ever so fine and sharp, are apt to disorder delicate substances. His knives, lancets, and styles were so fine that he could not see to sharpen them without the assistance of the microscope; but with them he could dissect the intestines of bees with the same accuracy and distinctness that others do those of large animals."

Swammerdam died when he was only forty-three. In the last years of his life his microscopes and tiny instruments lay neglected, for he had become a religious fanatic and had been persuaded somehow that science was evil.

Malpighi and Swammerdam both died early, having both perhaps burned out their lives by the intensity of their work, but Anton van Leeuwenhoek was not like them. He lived to the age of ninety-two, and worked all his years with gusto and robust good health. Malpighi had discovered minute things about the human body and plants and animals; and Swammerdam had first begun to understand the insect world; but Anton van Leeuwenhoek penetrated through lenses he himself had made into the mysterious world of the microbe. No one before his time had guessed that such tiny organisms existed.

A queer old man, this Anton van Leeuwenhoek. He lived all his life in Delft. He had hardly any education and never learned Latin, which in those days was the mark of an educated man. He worked when a boy as a clerk in a dry-goods shop. Part of his duty there was to examine textiles with a fine hand lens. Sometimes he placed the lens over other substances besides the cloth—the skin of his own hand, with little hairs protruding from it; the fiber of the wood on the table. Extraordinary! he must have thought. How different things look through a microscope!

Later he owned a dry-goods shop of his own, married, and brought up a family. But in his spare time he went to the spectacles-makers and learned from them how to grind lenses. The lenses he made were precise and beautiful. Altogether he made 247 instruments, and some of them would increase the size of a minute object as much as 270 times.

After he had learned to make the lenses, he learned something about metalwork so that he could mount them. He mounted the lenses of some of his microscopes in silver and gold, though it is hard to see where he got the money to pay for such precious metals.

When he was about forty he closed his dry-goods shop. He had had two wives, but they had both died, and his children were grown. He had been given the post of beadle in a church—work that did not require too much attention —and his daughter Maria kept house for him.

Now his happy days began. He took the microscopes he had made and looked at everything he could find—a hair, the brain of a fly, the wing of a moth, a bit of dust. He looked at such things over and over again, marveling. And his neighbors thought him a little queer, but one of them, sensing his genius, wrote to the Royal Society in London about him. The Royal Society invited him to correspond with them.

Not long after that he had indeed something to tell them. He had focused his microscope on a drop of water from a rain barrel, and had found in it, to his great astonishment, "little beasties" swimming about. Again and again he had seen the "wretched beasties." They were "moving about very nimbly because they were furnished with divers incredibly thin feet."

He began to write more and more about his discovery. He had found the little creatures not only in rain water but in pond water, and in the secretions of various animals, and even in the saliva of his own mouth. In long, rambling letters in Dutch, all interspersed with tales of his stupid neighbors and the doings of the town of Delft, he told of the "beasties" he had found.

"They stop, they stand still as 'twere upon a point, and then turn themselves round with that swiftness, as we see a top turn round, the circumference they make being no bigger than that of a fine grain of sand."

And later he wrote: "This last kind of animal is a thousand times smaller than the eye of a large louse."

Again he described: "An incredible number of little animals, of various sorts, which move very prettily, which tumble about and sidewise, this way and that."

The Royal Society did not believe him at first. But he wrote that many people in Delft had seen his "little beasties." He offered to send affidavits from "two men of God, one notary public, and eight other persons, worthy to be believed."

Would he send them one of his microscopes, then, or tell them how they had been made? This he would not do.

Then the Royal Society sent two of its most eminent members to see him; and he lifted down one of the hundred-odd microscopes from the cabinets that lined his room; and they saw what he had seen.

Leeuwenhoek was made a Fellow of the Royal Society after that. A whole succession of eminent people came to pay him their respects. One of them was Peter the Great of Russia.

He let his visitors look through his microscope, but kept a close watch lest one of the instruments be stolen. He continued to find all manner of strange little organisms, although he did not realize that they might have any connection with disease. He found other things. One day he found a human sperm, and said, according to one authority, that he saw a tiny small man in it with body, legs, and head. He discovered that vermin do not breed out of filth but come from eggs laid there by their predecessors. He discovered that plant aphids reproduce without fertilization by the male.

Occasionally, as in the matter of the human sperm, he could not resist making a good story of the things he saw. But generally he reported accurately, as a scientist should. He said: "My determination is not to remain stubbornly with my ideas but I'll leave them and go over to others as soon as I am shown plausible reasons which I can grasp. This is the more true since I have no other purpose than to place the truth before my eyes so far as it is in my power to embrace it; and to use the little talent I have received to draw the world away from its old heathenish superstitions and to go over to the truth, and to stick to it."

Old Anton van Leeuwenhoek's discovery of microbes was to start a new field of investigation. Many men were soon examining the "little beasties," arguing about their origin and their behavior. Louis Pasteur, in the nineteenth century, was to demonstrate the germ theory of disease and open up the whole new field of bacteriology.

But although Signor Malpighi, Jan Swammerdam, and Anton van Leeuwenhoek made very great contributions, their work lacked direction: it was scattered over so many different fields as to leave the scientists who followed them in a state of confusion. That is why, in the age that followed theirs, the natural scientists cared about nothing so much as classifying the information they had. That is why Linnaeus is important.

IX. "YOU ARE LINNAEUS!"

IN THE eighteenth century the world appeared more and more confusing. Besides the enormous variety of living organisms that men found by looking through their microscopes, travelers pushing into distant parts of the earth were bringing back plants and animals that the people of Europe had never seen before. Soon it became apparent that every part of the earth had its own plants, birds, and animals. Sometimes, too, ships' captains brought men and women from Africa or from the East, and from the Western Hemisphere. And though there was no doubt that these men and women were human beings, they were not like any of the people who had been seen in Europe before.

Science means, among other things, orderly, classified knowledge. So learned societies, universities, individual scholars tried to make some orderly arrangement of the vast and increasing store of knowledge. They made numberless efforts. One man thought he could classify plants according to the color of their blossoms, putting all those

85

with red blooms together and trying to see whether they were in any way alike. Another thought it would be better to arrange them according to their leaves—long leaves, round leaves, indented leaves. He worked very hard, but did not get on very well. There seemed to be too many plants whose leaves did not fit into any of his categories.

While these men were making fruitless efforts to classify plants, there were others who tried to establish some sort of order in the animal kingdom. They talked of the long-haired and the short-haired animals, those with horns and those without horns, and so on.

They studied fish and insects and crustaceans. All these efforts had the same result; and that was failure. So far as the men of the eighteenth century could see, there was no scheme or plan among the living things of the earth.

But, in the year 1707, Carl von Linné, later called Carolus Linnaeus, was born at Råshult in Småland, Sweden.

There was nothing striking about the boy's birth or his background. His father was the village pastor. The family lived in a small wooden house, painted red, with a roof of live turf. It was like many other houses in the village. But the house had a garden around it, so that Linnaeus was to say later that it was a good place for a naturalist to be born.

All the boy's teachers at school thought him stupid. But a doctor with whom his father talked observed that Carl

took an unusual interest in plants and that he could identify a great many. He suggested that his father send him
to a university, where he could study natural history. Perhaps later he would become a doctor. By such narrow
margins are great decisions reached.

His father could give him only about forty dollars for his
education, but it was thought that he could work his way.
So he set off for the University of Lund. After a year at
Lund he transferred to the University of Uppsala, since
Uppsala had a very fine course in botany. His professor
there was the venerable Olof Rudbeck. (*Rudbeckia hirta*,
or black-eyed Susans, have since been named for him.)

Professor Rudbeck soon grew very fond of Linnaeus and
saw great promise in his work. In his conversations with
his student the elderly professor often spoke enthusiastically of a journey to Lapland he had made in his youth. He
told of the reindeer, of the swift mountain streams fed by
the melting snows, of the mosses and lichens, the fir trees,
the snow fields, the midnight sun. Lapland, which had
been a land of romance for the old professor, became a
land of romance for the young student too.

After Linnaeus had finished his studies at the university,
with Professor Rudbeck's encouragement he made application to the Royal Society of Sweden to send him on a
scientific expedition to Lapland. Linnaeus wrote in the
letter of application that he was well qualified to go because, among other things, he had a knowledge of natural

history and his legs were so strong that he could walk and climb long distances.

Whether they were impressed by his knowledge, or by the strength of his legs, or by both, the Royal Society agreed to the commission. So, on May 12, 1732, at eleven o'clock in the morning, Linnaeus set out on foot through the gate of the old walled town of Uppsala on the road leading north.

"It was a splendid spring day," his diary records. "The sky was clear and warm, while the west wind refreshed one with a delicious breath. The winter rye stood six inches high, and the barley had newly come into leaf. The birch was beginning to shoot, and all the trees were leafing, except the elm and aspen. Though only a few of the spring flowers were in bloom, it was obvious that the whole land was smiling with the coming of spring. . . . When about eight miles had been traversed, the woods began to increase. The sweet lark which had hitherto delighted our ears, left us, another bird, the redwing, taking its place, which sang its sweetest from the fir tops, emulating the nightingale, the master singer."

The young Linnaeus must have made a cheerful figure as he strode along the road through the little villages and past the farms and on into the wild northern country. Another passage in his diary describes his equipment.

"My clothes consisted of a light coat of West Gothland linsey-woolsey cloth, without folds, lined with red shalloon, having small cuffs and a collar of shag; leather cap; and a pair of shag boots. I carried a small leather bag, half an ell in length but somewhat less in breadth, furnished on one side with hooks and eyes, so that it could be opened and shut at pleasure. This bag contained one shirt, two pairs of false sleeves, two half shirts, an inkstand, a pen case, microscope, and spyglass, a gauze cap to protect me occasionally from the gnats, a comb, my journal, and a parcel of paper stitched together for drying plants, both in folio, my manuscript ornithology, *Flora uplandica* and *Characteris generici*. I wore a hanger [sword] at my side, and carried a small fowling piece, as well as an octagonal stick graduated for the purpose of measuring."

His equipment was in fact not very different from that of a modern naturalist, except that fashions in clothes have changed since that day.

He traveled, mostly on foot, over bad roads and through wild country for nearly a thousand miles. Once a suspicious Laplander shot at him, but missed. Once at night he crossed a rushing stream on a raft and nearly lost his life when the logs of the raft parted.

But he got back to Uppsala in the autumn and gave the Royal Society a careful account of the things he had seen. In his report he noted the customs of the Lapps, whose ways were little known to the Swedes. He told of their clothes, of their huts mounted on poles, of their great herds of reindeer.

He also brought back pressed leaves of twenty-three kinds of willows, and described the pearl fishery at Purkejour; and he brought specimens of grasses that were resistant to the greatest cold; and forage plants which would color butter deep yellow, as well as directions for making ten different kinds of bread that could be used when grain failed.

Linnaeus presented his report to the Royal Society on November 9, 1732, and the members were greatly pleased with it. The minutes of the meeting on that date read:

"Herr Linnaeus' account of his journeys to and from Lapland, with its perils and labors, was read; it included the history of novelties in all three kingdoms of nature, which he supported with his catalogue."

But more important than his specimens and the information about Lapland, he brought notes on a new system of classification for plants and animals which he had worked out on his journey. Three years later this system was to be published under the title *Systema Naturae*. It was to bring order out of confusion. It was the system of nomenclature that has been used ever since.

According to Linnaeus' system, every plant and every animal was to be given a double Latin name. The first word—whose initial letter was to be capitalized—would indicate to what *genus* or general class it belonged. For example, there were in various countries large numbers of little plants resembling one another, which he called *Primula*, or primroses. This genus is almost worldwide. But one kind of primrose he called *Primula vulgaris.* Another, with purple flowers, he called *Primula farinosa*, and a third, which we would call a cowslip, he called *Primula veris.* So Linnaeus was able to christen hundreds of flowers, each time naming its genus first, and then adding the particular *species.*

He followed the same system with animals, recognizing easily the difference between the genus of horse or of cat, but indicating in the second part of the name the particular species to which it belonged. Whenever a species was identified, he encouraged the scientist who had first observed it to add his own name.

The naming of plants and animals in this way was a fascinating task. Linnaeus soon announced that everything in nature could be classified, if the scientists but had time and patience. Science, as orderly classified knowledge, was coming into its own. Linnaeus thought that he could even classify all minerals and all diseases.

The first edition of *Systema Naturae* was published in Leyden in 1735. It contained only twelve pages, but its influence was enormous.

A copy of the first edition was sent to Dr. Hermann Boerhaave, an eminent physician of Leyden, who had published Leeuwenhoek's work. Dr. Boerhaave introduced Linnaeus to the great London collector Sir Hans

Sloane and to various other notables of the scientific world. Everyone talked of Linnaeus; his fame spread everywhere.

In 1738 he went to Paris. His Swedish biographer, Fries, writes of him:

"On his arrival he went first to the Jardin des Plantes, where Bernard de Jussieu was describing in Latin some exotics, as rare plants were called. He entered without opportunity to introduce himself. There was one plant which the demonstrator had not yet determined and which seemed to puzzle him. The Swede looked on in silence, but, observing the hesitation of the learned professor, cried out, '*Haec planta faciem Americanum habet*'—'It has the appearance of an American plant.'

"Jussieu, surprised, turned about quickly and exclaimed, 'You are Linnaeus!' 'I am, sir!' was the reply. The lecture was stopped and Bernard gave the learned stranger an affectionate welcome!"

Gradually the boy who had been thought so stupid had become the most eminent natural scientist in Europe. He traveled; he married; he settled down at last at the University of Uppsala. There he took up the post of professor of botany which his old teacher Olof Rudbeck had held.

He made the teaching of botany enormously popular. Often he had as many as two or three hundred pupils in his classes. Students came from Germany, Italy, Russia, and other places to learn from him. Since the teaching was done in Latin, they had no difficulty in understanding his words.

The students in Linnaeus' classes became enthusiastic collectors and classifiers. He taught them not only to use his "binomial nomenclature" but to describe each plant according to a regular, orderly system; and he laid great stress on distinguishing as many species as possible. Even the most insignificant flower or weed deserved study and attention, he said. He taught that "there are as many species as issued in pairs from the hand of the Creator," and said that no new species had been added since the beginning of the world—an idea with which a modern biologist would certainly disagree.

He required his students to go on botanical excursions with him several times each week to collect plants and insects. Everything about the trips was carefully ordered and arranged. Students were to wear "easy" suits of linen and wide-brimmed hats to act as a protection from the sun. One of them was appointed annotator, to take down Linnaeus' dictation in case something new was identified. Another was to maintain discipline in the group.

Linnaeus himself was always first to arrive in the field, but by eight o'clock the two or three hundred students were assembled, and all day long they searched for specimens or gathered around him while he lectured.

At evening they marched back to the town, with Linnaeus at their head, while French horns and kettledrums played, and banners waved. When the parade finally reached the Botanic Garden at the University of Uppsala the group broke up, but not before the old university walls had resounded to the cry of "Viva Linnaeus!"

The field trips were a great joy to Linnaeus. He was fond of saying, "Mingle your joys sometimes with your earnest occupations"; and this both teacher and pupils succeeded in doing on their famous trips into the country.

The Botanic Garden was another of his satisfactions. He wanted to make it as beautiful as the famous Jardin des Plantes he had seen in France. He thought the Botanic Garden should be a kind of living library of plants, so that the public could learn their names and study them.

At one time he had as many as three thousand different species of plants in the Garden. The Empress Catherine of Russia sent him several hundred different kinds of seeds. People in distant places were encouraged to supply him with specimens of exotic plants. Some of them were sent all the way from Capetown in South Africa. He was much interested in trying to acclimatize plants, and made repeated efforts, though without success, to get Chinese tea to grow in Sweden.

After a time he decided to add birds and animals to the Garden. The Crown Prince of Sweden gave him an Indian bear, a "matchless cockatoo," and some guinea pigs. Later came an ape, a monkey, four kinds of parrots, an orangoutang, and some goldfish. Queen Louisa Ulrica gave him a cassowary that lived a long time in the Garden; and he was continually amused with the pranks of the monkeys. But he liked the parrots best, and especially one of them. "It used to sit on his shoulder," his biographer says, "sharing his meals. When therefore the parrot felt hungry it would say, 'Mr. Carl, it is twelve o'clock.'"

Many visitors came to the Garden to see the plants and animals and to talk to the brown-eyed gentleman who was its master. In 1769 Frederick Calvert, Lord Baltimore, on a European visit, rolled up to the door in a coach and four. He had gone to see Linnaeus before he visited the king, and was so delighted with what he saw in the Garden that he sent Linnaeus a gold snuffbox to commemorate the visit and a *necessaire* of silver to the value of three hundred pounds.

As the years passed, Linnaeus wrote several books on animals and plants, but none was more important than the little *Systema Naturae* that he had worked out on his Lapland journey. Scholars everywhere spoke his name with great respect now. He was Sweden's great man. The Swedish Parliament gave him a title.

At seventy he was still hale and hearty. He suffered sometimes from gout, but he said he knew how to control it by eating wild strawberries.

He died in 1778. The botanical and zoological gardens fell into decay. His widow sold all his papers and writings to a British collector. The King of Sweden, on hearing that they were to be taken out of the country, dispatched a sloop to try to overtake the vessel that carried them, but the vessel got away. The papers have been considered ever since a great treasure of the Linnaean Society in London.

But though his gardens fell into decay and his writings were taken to London, his students continued the work he had begun. From his classroom and from the fields of his botanical excursions they scattered everywhere, collecting, examining, classifying. One of them went to the far South Seas, another to Antarctica. In Africa, in Asia, in the Western Hemisphere, they were pointing, as Linnaeus had done, to the beauty and the intricacy of the living world.

And like their master Linnaeus, they were pointing to the endless variety of species. They had not yet begun to ask what makes one species of an animal or plant differ from another. That was to come later.

X. THE BARON AND THE FOSSILS

IN THE years following Linnaeus' death the system of
giving plants, animals, birds, and fish double Latin
names was enthusiastically carried forward. People carrying tin boxes to hold botanical specimens scoured the
woods and fields to bring home and classify hundreds and
hundreds of plants. They collected mosses and ferns, and
vied with one another to find new kinds of mushrooms.
They arranged and named large numbers of shells and
fish and insects.

97

The animals were more difficult to arrange than other living things, because they varied more in different parts of the world. No one questioned why this was. They were content simply to accept the fact. It was, for example, easy to distinguish a member of the cat family, and to name it *Felis*. It was, moreover, easy to see that one kind of cat had the smooth, tawny coat of a lion, and therefore easy to call it *Felis leo,* while another had the striped coat of a tiger, and could be called *Felis tigris.* But then it seemed that a lion from one place looked different from a lion of another place, so they added a third name, and this usually indicated the place the lion had come from. It was not a double name now but a triple one, *Felis leo senegalensis.*

Baron Georges Cuvier, inspector of education in France in Napoleon's time, thought there was too much emphasis on classifying and naming things.

"What difference does it make," he said, "what you call them? The business of the scientist is to understand, not to name."

In a sense he was wrong, of course, for Linnaeus and his followers had done a great service. Still, Cuvier had his own contribution to make, and it was perhaps natural that he thought other men's contributions unimportant.

Baron Cuvier was a striking person; whatever he said demanded attention. The glittering decorations Napoleon had given him; his erect, imposing stature, his waving white hair; his beautiful uniforms—all proclaimed the leader, the man of assurance, the man whose opinions were not to be disputed. He was as efficient in his scientific work as he was in the important government projects he undertook.

A large staff of students and assistants carried out the details of Cuvier's researches. And he had a knack for enlisting the help of anyone with whom he came in contact, even the visitors in his own household. In the morning, before he set off in his carriage to perform the important tasks his various political offices required, he set the guests in his household to copying plates that illustrated animal life. When he returned in the evening he never failed to inquire whether they were finished, and to inspect them.

Of course he had not always been so important. His life started quite humbly. His father was a retired officer of the Swiss army who made his home in Alsace-Lorraine. His mother had the great admiration for learning that is sometimes found in those who have little schooling. She taught her son to read, sent him to an elementary school, and heard him recite his Latin lessons every day, though she knew no Latin herself. All through the pomp and grandeur of his later years Baron Cuvier remembered his mother affectionately. Her favorite flowers had been red stocks, and his friends observed that throughout his life he kept a vase of these flowers on his desk.

It is not known how his mother managed to give him the money to buy books, but it is certain that during his boyhood he owned at least one book that was important to him. It was a thick volume by Konrad Gesner, a Swiss naturalist and physician who lived about the time of Vesalius. The book was called *Historia Animalium*. It was a huge volume containing all the knowledge of animals that had been discovered up to that time. Most of the information was based on fact, although it must be confessed that the book gave a long account of mermaids. Gesner's book was beautifully illustrated with woodcuts, and the young Cuvier spent much time in coloring these according to the descriptions given in the text.

The other book Cuvier treasured was a natural history of the earth written by a distinguished, powerful, and wealthy Frenchman, the Comte de Buffon. This book he did not own, for it had been issued in twenty-two volumes. He found it one day in the library of a relative, and after that it occupied a great place in his thoughts. In this book Buffon had tried to set down what he called the seven epochs of the earth's history. The first he called the "incandescent" stage; the fifth the coming of rhinoceroses, hippopotamuses, and elephants; the seventh the coming of man.

Buffon's ideas appealed especially to Cuvier, for even in his very young days he liked things on a grand scale. The vastness of Buffon's conceptions impressed him

greatly. It was to be written of him later: *"Ce qui carac-
terise partout M. Cuvier c'est l'esprit vaste"*—"What particularly characterizes Monsieur Cuvier is the grandeur of
his spirit."

When he was twelve years old, then, Cuvier knew as
much about animals as Gesner and Buffon could teach
him. He carried a volume of one or the other around in his
pocket and was constantly copying pictures of birds, insects, plants, and animals. For several of his sketches he
received prizes, to his mother's great pride.

Now, through the good offices of Duke Charles, uncle
of the king of Württemberg, he was sent to the Academy
of Stuttgart. That was when he was fourteen years old.
Not much is known of his life at the academy, but after he
had finished the course there he became tutor to the son
of the Comte d'Héricy, and lived six years near Caen on
the coast of Normandy.

Those were the years of the French Revolution, and a
number of eminent royalists had taken refuge in Normandy. One of these men introduced Cuvier to friends at
the Jardin du Roi, the great botanic garden in Paris that
had been started by Louis XIV. Cuvier could hardly believe his good fortune when, after the Revolution, he
received an appointment at the Jardin.

Soon after this he was brought to the attention of
Napoleon, who invited him to go as a naturalist on his
Egyptian campaign. Cuvier must have refused the offer

gracefully, for soon Napoleon was offering him other distinctions. In 1813 he was appointed Commissaire Imperial Extraordinaire. In 1814 he became a member of the Council of State. In 1819 he became a baron, in 1831 a peer.

All the while his circle of friends grew larger, his house more impressive, his decorations more brilliant, his uniforms more beautiful. (There was one uniform of violet silk with embroideries of his own design.) And all the while his interest in natural history paralleled his political and worldly advances.

If he was a baron, an inspector of education, a professor of anatomy, he was also a scientist. Perhaps he considered himself a scientist first.

The field that engrossed him most deeply was anatomy. Bones and skeletons, the scaffolding on which bodies are built, held an endless fascination for him.

Most anatomists before Cuvier's time had been physicians, and had started with a study of the human body. After that they had compared other forms of life to it. Cuvier, however, started with the simplest forms. At Caen he had studied marine life: fishes, mollusks, and worms. When he came to Paris he made special investigations of rhinoceroses, elephants, and lemurs. And finally he studied the skeleton of man.

While he was working with all these shells and bones, his great plan began to take form. He never completed it, but with its beginning comparative anatomy was born. His ideas were put forward in several speeches and pamphlets, and were finally published in a famous book called *Le Règne Animal Distribué d'après son Organisation— The Animal Kingdom Arranged according to its Organization.*

Cuvier believed that all animal life should be divided into four great groups. These were the vertebrates, the articulates or jointed creatures (crustaceans and insects), the mollusks, and the radiates, such as starfish and jellyfish.

He did not try to guess what the essence of life was— that was a riddle no one could guess, he said. Life, he thought, could spring only from previous life, and how it was produced was beyond our grasp. The four great types of animals, however, were well defined. Each species within its own broad order was unchangeable, giving birth to its kind without variation. Species were immutable, he proclaimed.

It happened that in Paris after the Revolution a great deal of building was going forward. The stone for the new buildings was limestone, which occurred in well-defined layers. Geology was a new study at that time, but scientists all agreed that the various layers of rock represented various ages in the world's history.

In these layers of rock, as the builders cut into them, great numbers of fossil bones appeared. Cuvier determined

to study them. He organized a group of scientific workers
to sort and examine the fossils.

It was an absorbing matter to take the fossil bones from
the layers of rock where they had lain so long and to try
to fit them together. For a long time Cuvier had been developing a theory of correlation of the parts of an animal's
body. If the animal had a certain type of jaw, he noticed,
it would have a certain type of hoof, a certain type of
alimentary canal. Now, with the fossil bones, when he
had fitted them together, he was able to deduce what the
soft parts of the animal that had lived so long ago had
been like. This is the science of paleontology, and Cuvier
has been called its founder.

But as he assembled the skeletons of the animals of the
past and saw how altogether strange they were to a more
modern eye a troubling question rose. Why were these animals so different from the ones he could see around him?
If, as he had believed and taught, the species were immutable, if each creature gave birth to another after its
own kind, why were there no longer creatures in the
neighborhood of Paris like those whose bones had been
dug up?

Baron Cuvier, the orderly, careful, systematic professor
of anatomy, had to make a theory to suit what he believed
to be the facts. He was sure that species never changed
from one generation to another; therefore he had to find
some other explanation. He said—and because he was so

distinguished and influential large numbers of young scientists believed him—that the animals whose fossil bones he had studied had been destroyed in some great catastrophe. There had in fact been several such catastrophes in the world's history. Destruction had overwhelmed the earth. The mountains had tumbled into the sea; the ocean waters had swept across the land; all living things had been destroyed. In Egypt, in Chaldea and Palestine, legends persisted still to prove that this was true.

Cuvier believed that isolated parts of the earth, little islands in the sea perhaps, might have been spared in the great catastrophes. From them living creatures may have crept forth to propagate their kind and repeople the earth. But the prehistoric animals whose fossil bones he had assembled had been destroyed forever.

Most of the scientists of his time believed in Cuvier's theory of catastrophes, but there were some who objected to it. At the French Academy of Sciences in 1830, Geoffroy Saint-Hilaire protested that species changed with passing generations. Baron Cuvier listened to him in astonishment. It was incredible that anyone should question his theories! Then he rose slowly, walked to a blackboard at the front of the room where the meeting was held, and began to draw diagrams illustrating his theory. Geoffroy Saint-Hilaire and those like him were silenced—at least for a time.

Jean Baptiste Pierre Lamarck had been saying for years

that species change with the passage of time, but he did not have the authority or the importance of Baron Cuvier. In 1832, however, Baron Cuvier died of the plague that swept through Paris. After his death people began to consider whether what Lamarck was saying might, after all, have some truth in it.

XI. LAMARCK
AND THE LADDER OF LIFE

WHILE Baron Cuvier was studying his fossils, Jean
Baptiste Lamarck was seeking unobtrusively to understand the relationship of living things. In fact, though
he was a contemporary of Cuvier, he began his work earlier
than did the eminent baron, for he was working in France
at the time of the French Revolution.

In the summer of 1760 Lamarck was sixteen years old.

That summer he inherited a small legacy from his father. It did not amount to much, for Lamarck was the eleventh son of an impoverished nobleman. Actually the amount of the inheritance was just enough to enable Lamarck to buy a horse. Thereupon he left the Jesuit college at Amiens where he had been studying theology, and, riding his new mount, set off to join the French army, which was then engaged in fighting the Germans in the Seven Years' War.

He rode along the poplar-lined road across the plains of Picardy in northern France; and the level fields of barley and rye were sprinkled with poppies and blue cornflowers. Behind him he left his birthplace, Bazantin, its church, its little town hall, its grocery, the two-storied house in which he had been born.

So he traveled down through France toward the south to the place where his regiment was encamped. The day after he reached it a major battle was fought. The battle was so fierce that it nearly destroyed his regiment. All the officers were killed, and the men were thrown into panic and confusion. There would have been a general rout had not the young Lamarck managed to hold them together until help arrived. The French commanders were so impressed with what he had done that they gave him a commission as lieutenant. It looked then as if a career in the army awaited him.

But once again his plans changed. One day in the barracks a comrade in play lifted him by his head. The lymphatic glands in his neck were injured and it was necessary for him to go to Paris for treatment. So he was discharged from the army.

In Paris he began to study medicine. To pay his expenses he worked as a clerk in a bank; and he lived in a garret in the Latin Quarter. He lived thus for about four years. In his garret room he grew interested in meteorology through watching the movement of clouds from his window. They were the only natural objects he could see. But on Sundays it was his habit to walk in the woods and fields outside Paris. On one of these walks he met Jean Jacques Rousseau, and after that they went on botanizing trips together.

Jean Jacques Rousseau with his gospel of Nature was a great figure in France at that time. People said it was he who made the study of plants and flowers *à la mode*. But Fashion certainly held little interest for the young bank clerk. For from the day he met Rousseau the study of plants was an absorbing passion with him. With the same courage that had enabled him to hold on until help was brought to his shattered company, now, in spite of poverty, he managed somehow to hold onto this study, which seemed to him the most important thing in the world.

He became a student of botany under Bernard de Jussieu, the same professor who had received Linnaeus so enthusiastically. Soon he had begun a new classification of plants, thinking, rather boldly perhaps, that he could improve on Linnaeus. His idea was to divide the various

species into subspecies so that a student could first determine the large group to which a plant belonged and then
place it in one of its various subgroups.

In ten years' time he was ready to publish his small book
called *Flore française,* which he believed would help students to identify the flowers it described. The title page
describes it as "A succinct description of all the plants
growing naturally in France."

The book brought Lamarck recognition immediately.
Everyone in scientific circles was talking of the brilliant
new botanist. The distinguished Comte de Buffon, whose
book had so inspired Cuvier, arranged to have Lamarck
admitted to the French Academy of Sciences and invited
him to make a tour of Europe with his young son, with
the purpose of visiting museums and botanical gardens.

But on his return, though he was now famous, he continued to be very poor. The Comte de Buffon, who had
influence at court, succeeded in having him appointed as
keeper of the herbarium at the Jardin du Roi.

The wages of the keeper of the herbarium were misera-
bly small, but Lamarck was thankful to have work that
was connected with the plants he loved. He was thirty-
three, and strikingly handsome, especially when at meet-
ings of the French Academy of Sciences he wore his high
white stock and the heavily embroidered coat of an Academy member. In his quick mind a hundred theories were
developing—ideas not alone of botany, but of chemistry

and of the origin of the globe and its atmosphere. Occasionally he presented his ideas to the Academy. The members listened to him tolerantly; perhaps they were a little amused at his ardor.

But for all his imagination and enthusiasm, he could not climb beyond the lowly post of keeper of the herbarium.

Then the French Revolution turned France upside down. The king and his court were swept away. The sound of the carts rumbling toward the guillotine could be heard from the quiet room where Lamarck worked. Word reached him that Lavoisier, the chemist, had been beheaded.

But Lamarck's post was such a humble one that he seemed quite unimportant, and the revolutionists did not disturb him. When the fighting was over, the French government wanted to change everything that had been associated with the old regime. So they accepted Lamarck's suggestion of renaming the Jardin du Roi the Jardin des Plantes, and planned to offer courses there to promising young students.

They decided to engage two professors of zoology, and offered one of these professorships to Lamarck. The other was to go to Geoffroy Saint-Hilaire. Geoffroy was later to dispute with Baron Cuvier, but at this time he was only twenty-two.

Lamarck was in his fiftieth year when he received the appointment. He had spent more than twenty-five years in the study of botany. A less adventurous man might have hesitated at trying to master a subject that was wholly new and about which no one had very much knowledge. But Lamarck believed that living things should be studied as a whole. He had been a botanist; the next logical step for him was to investigate the animal world. It was Lamarck who invented the term *biology,* by which he meant the study of all living things, both animal and plant.

At the Jardin des Plantes he divided the work in zoology with young Geoffroy Saint-Hilaire. Geoffroy agreed to work with birds and mammals; Lamarck with "insects, worms, and microscopic animals."

A museum publication listed him thus: "Lamarck: fifty years old; married for the second time; . . . professor of zoology, of insects, of worms and microscopic animals."

His laboratory was a confusing place. Here, amid specimens from Africa and Europe, from Asia and America, he tried to find some orderly method of arrangement. Linnaeus, he knew, had simply lumped all insects and worms together. But there were thousands of species of insects and worms, and Linnaeus had never even examined the "little beasties" that Leeuwenhoek had seen. Living things were related to one another, Lamarck was sure. But *how* were they related?

Finally he hit upon a plan. He thought all animals might be classified according to their fundamental organs —their lungs, their hearts, their nervous systems. This

could be done with the vertebrate animals; and perhaps
the invertebrates could be arranged in a similar way. In
his mind's eye he began to see a great ladder, upon whose
rungs, step by step, all living things found their places.

He was excited by the idea. He hardly dared to tell
anyone about it until he had gone further. Day after day
he worked with microscopes and with dissecting instruments, examining hearts, lungs, nervous systems. Finally
he was ready. It was almost too good to be true. The
ladder of life was there. Step by step he could see the
progression from one species to another.

This was a great discovery, he thought. He must present
it to the members of the Institute of France. But not before
it was ready. He would publish his findings, but undoubtedly the work would require many volumes. And he did
not know how he would get the money to pay for its
publication. But he would find it somehow. The thing to
do was to begin.

He decided after some deliberation to start at the top
of his ladder with the mammals. They were more familiar
to most people than the simple little creatures at the other
end of the scale. At the top, then, he placed men, apes,
horses, dogs, and other mammals. They were the most intelligent of all creatures; they had backbones, heads that
could be moved around, eyes with eyelids, hearts with two
chambers, and warm blood.

Birds, which he placed on the next step, also had hearts

with two chambers and warm blood. They also were intelligent. But they did not have the organs of reproduction of mammals; they laid eggs.

Below the birds he placed the reptiles. Their hearts had only a single chamber and their lungs were simpler. They had spinal columns and nervous systems. But their blood was cold.

Then came the fish. They had gills but rarely lungs. They had no true voices, no eyelids. But they had backbones, separate heads, and nervous systems.

Below the fish, backbones were gone. Now, Lamarck said, come the *"animaux sans vertèbres."* These creatures did not breathe with lungs, had no voices, no real blood. Among the invertebrates, as he called the animals without backbones, there was the same "stepping down." First were mollusks, such as oysters and clams. Oysters breathed by means of gills, like fish, and had nerves. Then came the annelids, as Lamarck called a certain class of marine worms. They breathed through gills that were sometimes hidden under the skin.

Lamarck went on examining and arranging one class after another, from the crustaceans to the spiders; and to the insects; and then to the worms, which had no organs of sight or hearing and no tongues; and after that to the radiates, such as the starfish; and finally to the polyps, at the bottom of the scale, the simplest of all creatures. The polyps, he noted, had no special organs of feeling, no

breathing, no circulation, no reproductive organs. They
had nothing but a single alimentary canal, and could
absorb nourishment through any part of their bodies. They
were almost formless, like globules of gelatin. Yet they
were the beginning, Lamarck was sure—the beginning
from which all the rest developed.

As Lamarck worked on he became more and more sure
that one form of life had developed from another.

"Citizens," he wrote, "go from the simplest to the most
complex, and you will have the true thread that connects
all the productions of nature; you will have an accurate
idea of progression; you will be convinced that the simplest of living things give rise to all the others."

So, fifty-seven years before Darwin's great book, *The
Origin of Species,* was published, Lamarck grasped the
idea of evolution that scientists have held ever since.

But how did it all come about? Lamarck asked himself.
What makes one species change and develop into another?

In a leaflet called *Recherches sur l'organisation des corps
vivants* he gave his explanation. "I have no thought of
producing a work of importance," he wrote, "but only of
publishing my lecture in leaflet form to those who might
be interested in my observations."

Why has evolution occurred, he asked. It is because the
animal with the passage of time has changed to adapt itself
to its environment. "It is not the organs—that is, the character and form of the animal's body parts—that have given

rise to its habits and particular structures. It is the habit and manner of life and the conditions in which its ancestors lived that have in the course of time fashioned its bodily form, its organs and qualities." This is the so-called theory of acquired characteristics.

Where an organ has been used, he said, it has developed; where it has fallen into disuse, it has dwindled away; and changes brought about in this way give rise to changes in the species. The polyp, through the effect of its environment, changes with the passing of countless ages of time to become one of the radiates, the radiates become worms, the worms in time turn into insects, and so on up the scale to the top of the ladder, where the mammals are. And examples of all these are in existence at any given moment, but all are constantly changing, evolving.

For nothing is stationary, Lamarck saw. All the things in the universe are moving and changing. The surface of the earth, the waters of the sea, the animals and fish, the trees and plants, are in a continual slow process of change.

He took a giraffe as an example. "We know that this tallest of mammals, living in arid localities, is obliged to browse on the foliage of trees. It has resulted from this habit, maintained over a long period of time, that in all the individuals of the race the forelegs have become longer than the hinder ones, and that the neck is so elongated that it raises the head almost six meters [twenty feet] in height."

So Lamarck saw that through long stretches of time, as the earth was continually changing, animals and men changed too. And he gave what explanation he could of the reason for this. His theory of the inheritance of acquired characteristics is discussed in some places still.

In his own time no one paid much attention to his theories. Cuvier, disdainful, dismissed his notions as "a new piece of madness." Geoffroy Saint-Hilaire was the only one who believed in him. The neglect of his fellow scientists did not matter to Lamarck. He had never expected much acclaim. For thirty-five years he worked at the great book on vertebrates and invertebrates that he had begun when he was fifty. He was very poor. He had lost four wives by death. In the last years of his life he was completely blind. But he kept on with his work by dictating to his daughter Cornèlie, who acted as nurse, housekeeper, and secretary for him.

People hardly noticed when he died. Cornèlie was free to put down her pencil and go out for a walk in the sun. And there was a meeting at the Academy with rather perfunctory eulogies. Geoffroy Saint-Hilaire grieved for the old man, for he had loved him and believed in him.

But Lamarck had finished his work. The sixth volume of the book on zoology was done.

And Charles Darwin, half a century later, spoke again, as many others were doing, of evolution. But he had a different idea of how species changed.

XII. THE BIRTH AND GROWTH OF DARWIN'S THEORY

AS EVERYONE knows, a part of the story of the creation of the earth is given in the Book of Genesis, as follows:

And God said, Let the earth bring forth grass, the herb yielding seed, and the fruit tree yielding fruit after his kind, whose seed is in itself upon the earth . . .

And God created great whales, and every living creature that moveth, which the waters brought forth abundantly, after their kind, and every winged fowl after his kind . . .

And God said, Let the earth bring forth the living creature after his kind, cattle and creeping thing, and beast of the earth after his kind . . .

Until about the 1860s most people took the words of the Book of Genesis as literally true. They believed that these words were an account of what they called "special creation"; that every kind of plant and animal had been created in those first days of the world; that all living things "after [their] kind" had come down exactly as they were made, generation after generation.

It was true that the Greeks in the fourth century B.C. had talked of organisms that changed from one generation to the other, but their ideas had been forgotten. Later Baron Cuvier, looking at fossils embedded in strata of rock, had talked of catastrophes that destroyed the life of a whole generation and made a new creation necessary. Lamarck had thought that all living things were related and that one species developed from another. But no one in his time thought much of Lamarck and his theories. There had been only a few others who regarded the Book of Genesis as poetry and not as a factual account of creation. Even most scientists up to the end of the nineteenth century accepted the fact of "special creation" without question.

Then Charles Darwin brought the idea of organic evolution sharply to people's attention. It was he who proposed a theory of how and why one species developed from another. In 1859 his great book *The Origin of Species* was published, and after that people's whole outlook on nature seemed to change.

It was rather strange that Darwin should have worked out the theory of organic evolution, for at first he believed in "special creation" as firmly as anyone could. In the beginning he had no thought of being a naturalist. His father, in fact, was quite discouraged with him, for in his early years he seemed to care for nothing but horseback-riding and pheasant-shooting. His father feared that he would become "nothing but an idle sportsman."

Finally, however, Darwin agreed to study at the medical school of the University of Edinburgh, for both his father and his grandfather were doctors. But the lectures at the medical school appeared to him dull, and he could not bear the sight of operations; they were administered in those days without anesthetics. So he left the medical school.

After that—and there was a good deal of argument first—he agreed to study for the ministry. He thought he might become a country minister. He loved country life, and had begun some collections of beetles and butterflies. Reluctantly, then, he enrolled as a theological student at Cambridge. And there he met Professor John Stevens Henslow, the geologist and botanist.

Almost immediately Henslow and Charles Darwin became fast friends. They were seen walking together so often that the students at Cambridge called Darwin "the man who walks with Henslow."

It was during those years, and under Henslow's influence, that Darwin began to read the works of the great naturalists. He read of Alexander von Humboldt's *Personal Narrative of Travels to the Equinoctial Regions of America* and longed to set foot in the new world. He read Sir John Herschel's *Introduction to the Study of Natural*

Philosophy and dreamed of adding something humble but substantial perhaps to what he called a little pompously, "the noble structure of natural science."

His opportunity to add to that structure came much more quickly than he anticipated. In the late summer of 1831, the HMS *Beagle* was to make a cruise around the world for purposes of mapping and scientific observation. The captain, Robert Fitzroy, wanted a scientist to go on the expedition—"a scientific person to examine the land."

Professor Henslow recommended Charles Darwin for the post, and Darwin was filled with excitement. To go to the equinoctial regions of America as Von Humboldt had done, to have a chance to examine minerals and wild life in regions where he had never been before, seemed to him the opportunity of his life.

But his father objected. The boy ought to finish his theological course, he said. He had wasted time enough. Charles Darwin's uncle, Josiah Wedgwood, who was the owner of the famous Wedgwood potteries, saw the youth's point of view. He had his horses harnessed to his carriage and drove more than thirty miles to see the elder Darwin. In the end the permission was given, and Charles Darwin set off for the *Beagle*.

But now he encountered another difficulty. The captain of the vessel hesitated to accept him. He doubted, he said, "whether a man with such a shaped nose could possess sufficient energy and determination for the voyage."

"How strange!" Charles Darwin said years later. "I became a naturalist only because my uncle was willing to
drive thirty miles to see my father, and because the captain finally decided he did not object to the shape of my
nose."

His Majesty's ship *Beagle,* a ten-ton brig, sailed out of
Devonport on the twenty-seventh of December, 1831. She
was bound for Patagonia, and thence through the straits
of Tierra del Fuego, and so on around the world. "It was
the most important event in my life," Charles Darwin
wrote years later.

The little brig pushed out across the Atlantic, and soon
she was encountering rough seas, so that the young naturalist, lying in his bunk, was miserable with seasickness.
This sickness was to plague him off and on, whenever the
vessel rocked, throughout the five years of the voyage.

They landed on the South American coast, and Darwin
began his collections immediately. Soon he had minerals,
shells, and plants arranged systematically in the small
room behind the mast where he also kept his books and
instruments. Since the space alloted him was so small, he
decided not to collect many specimens but to choose each
one as carefully as he could and classify it in as orderly a
way as possible.

Day after day the vessel sailed along the South American
coast, and the young naturalist, who had never been out

of England before, watched the unfolding panorama of the South American shore—the dark Brazilian forests with their rich life of birds, reptiles, and animals; the high grass of the pampas in Argentina; the bleak, rocky heights of Patagonia, where the wind never stopped blowing. For though the *Beagle* was to push on across the Pacific and into the South Seas, the greater part of her voyage was spent along the coast of South America.

As they sailed down the coast Darwin went ashore at frequent intervals to study the land, the mud, the rocks, the fossil bones, the fungi in the dark forests, the ostrich on the high plains, the flamingo that fed on the worms of the salt lakes of Argentina.

When the *Beagle* laid over for a month at one of the Galapagos Islands, five hundred miles from the South American coast, strange and disturbing thoughts began to enter Charles Darwin's mind. On this island, which was composed of volcanic lava recently cast up from the sea, he said he felt himself "placed in proximity to the very act of creation itself." Here he found animals that were certainly of the same genera as those on the mainland of South America. Yet they were not the same; they seemed to be of different species. And as the *Beagle* moved on, visiting one island after another, he found that each island had its separate species of plants and animals.

Now, he thought, watching the rim of the ocean as the little vessel pushed across the sea, why had a separate species been created for each small island? The making of such a multiplicity of species seemed at least irrational. Why were there thousands of different species on those islands? Why did they belong to the genera of South America, which was miles away? Seeds might have been blown across from the mainland to the islands by the winds; animals might perhaps have swum across. But if this was true, why was each of the species on the islands a little different from those on the mainland?

The problem troubled him. Characteristically he said nothing about it, however. In a small yellow notebook he started to make notes on his observations.

After he reached England again he wrote to Joseph Dalton Hooker, the botanist: "At last gleams of light have come, and I am almost convinced (quite contrary to the opinion I started with) that species are not (it is like confessing a murder) immutable."

But the confession of the "murder" was later. For the present he was simply examining the facts.

Finally the *Beagle* docked at Falmouth, October 2, 1836, and Darwin, who had suffered from seasickness almost every day of the five-year voyage, found himself on firm land again. The voyage was over.

Darwin's letters and part of his specimens had arrived in England before him, and his reputation as a naturalist was now well established. The scientists greeted him enthusiastically. Charles Lyell, the Scotch geologist, whose book Darwin had carried all the way around the world, now became his friend. Joseph Dalton Hooker was eager to know him. Robert Brown, the Australian microscopist, showed him discoveries he had made with his lens. The great German naturalist Von Humboldt, then visiting England, asked to meet him. Thomas Carlyle and Thomas Babington Macaulay made much of him.

But Charles Darwin wanted to get away from all of them. After three years in London, he married his first cousin, Hannah Wedgwood, and they bought a roomy, comfortable house with a garden at Down, a small town in Kent. There he was to live and work for the rest of his life.

The problem that Charles Darwin wanted to study was the one that had perplexed him first on board the *Beagle*. Had the God whose "special creation" he had taken so much for granted really created so many thousands of species, all of them so nearly alike, yet different? Or was it possible that the idea of special creation might be wrong? Was there some sort of relationship between the species? He had heard of the work of Lamarck, but he thought nothing of it—"rubbish" he called it. Cuvier's idea of catastrophes seemed to him foolish too.

He decided that he might get some help by studying domestic animals, since these were near at hand and easy to observe. He began a correspondence with a large number of breeders and started to breed different races of pigeons himself. He found that man could certainly modify the breeds of dogs, of cows, of pigeons. There must be some force in nature that works the same way, he thought. But what was it?

Then one day in his study at Down he happened to pick up and read "for diversion" a book by the English minister Thomas Malthus. The book was called *An Essay on the Principle of Population*. Reading that book made Darwin see the solution of his own problem.

For Malthus pointed out that the population of the earth was continually growing by geometric progression. If war, hunger, and disease did not kill off a part of the people in each generation, there would hardly be room for them to stand on the earth. There would certainly not be food enough to feed them.

Something like that must happen in all nature, Darwin thought. All organisms must increase at an enormous rate. Linnaeus had said somewhere that if a plant produced two seeds each year, and if each of these produced only two seeds in the same way, a million plants would be descended from the first one in only twenty years. Darwin kept thinking of that. And take animals, he argued. An elephant is a very slow breeder. But if a pair of elephants produce six young in the course of their lives, and each of these does likewise, in seven hundred and fifty years there will be nineteen million elephants on the earth! They would have a struggle to keep alive, he said.

This, then, might be the answer, he thought—a continual struggle to exist. But granted, as he could easily observe, that every member of a species is not exactly like every other, granted that there are some variations among them, what determines which ones will survive? What determines which plants or birds or animals will live and which will die off? How is the balance so beautifully kept that the world is never overrun with elephants or stifled with oak trees?

The answer he found to his problem came to him slowly, as he sat in his comfortable library with its book-lined walls, as he walked through his garden at Down, as he watched his cattle cropping the grass in his pastures.

He could not tell exactly why there was a slight variation in the offspring of each plant or animal. That slight variation will "provide a grand and hitherto untrodden field of investigation," he said. But it is certain that some green beetles are a little greener than others; some swallows have stronger wings than others; some deer are quicker to hear the sound of danger. And among these, those that are best fitted to adapt themselves to their environment survive and reproduce their kind, while the others die off. By piling up variations in one direction over long ages of time, new species are formed.

The idea of special creation now seemed like an idle dream to him. As he walked through his fields, often accompanied by his terrier, Polly, he examined plant and animal, bird and insect, considering his theory as he went along.

The years went by. He was still testing, examining. He wanted to be sure of his facts; he wanted to accumulate scores of facts. Sometimes he wrote his friends about what he was trying to do. In 1842 he wrote his friend Sir Joseph Dalton Hooker, "I have been ever since my return engaged in a very presumptuous work and I know no one individual who would not say a very foolish one. . . ."

In 1844 he wrote out in pencil a brief statement of his new theory and showed it to a few friends. They urged him to hasten to publish it. But he said there were more data that must be collected: he wanted to be so sure that he was right.

Then, in June, 1858, a letter arrived from Alfred Russel Wallace, a naturalist working in Malaya. Wallace had worked out exactly the same theory!

Darwin was a generous man, and not ambitious. He thought that Wallace should publish his findings and receive the credit for them. "I would far rather burn my whole book than that he [Wallace] or any other man should think I had behaved in a paltry spirit."

But Darwin's friends, Lyell and Hooker, knew that he had been working on his theory for years, though he had never officially published it. They proposed, therefore, that both Darwin and Wallace should be given credit for the theory; and this was done. At the Linnaean Society in

London on July 1, 1858, papers written by both Darwin and Wallace announcing the theory of evolution and the survival of the fittest were read.

In 1859 Darwin published his famous book, *The Origin of Species*. And it was followed in 1871 by another book, called *The Descent of Man*. In the latter book he applied the doctrine of the survival of the fittest to human beings, and drew the conclusion that "man is descended from some less highly organized form."

The uproar that followed the publication of Darwin's theories must have been heard even in the quiet garden of the house at Down. For most people are conservative and do not like to see their well-established ideas upset. Some of the churchmen objected to his rashness in questioning the doctrine of special creation. Some of them thought that he implied that men were descended from apes, though actually he had never said any such thing. What he had said was that all human beings were descended from a common ancestor. Still, in England, on the continent of Europe, and in America, the controversy he had stirred up raged on.

He grew to be an old man, who walked about his garden in a long black cloak, his beard snowy white, but his gray eyes still keen beneath their overhanging brows.

He died in 1882, and his countrymen took his body to Westminster Abbey, where they buried him beside Sir Isaac Newton.

And still the controversy about his theory raged. But gradually, one after another, the voices of his enemies were quieted. Gradually his ideas were accepted. And though his theory was amplified and changed as the years passed, organic evolution is still the idea on which modern science is built.

Theodosius Dobzhansky, a present-day biologist, has written: "We now think the things we see around us were not always as they are now, but evolved gradually from very different-looking ancestors; that these ancestors were in general less complex, less perfect, and less diversified than the organisms now living; that the evolutionary process is still under way; and that the causes can therefore be studied by observation and experiment in the field and in the laboratory."

That is exactly what Darwin thought nearly a hundred years ago. The work of the biologists since his time has been very largely an attempt to elaborate his theory.

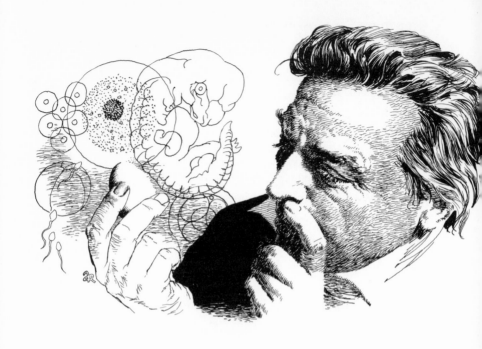

XIII. VON BAER AND HIS EMBRYOS

"IF I COULD study an organism from its very beginning, if I could watch it from the very first instant the
sperm enters the egg and study all the stages that it passes
through till it becomes a complete adult, then I might
understand how an animal's body is built; and this surely
is one of the most extraordinary things in nature." This, in
substance, is what Karl Ernst von Baer said.

Von Baer knew, of course, that among the simpler organisms reproduction is brought about by cell division.

But with the plants that are more complex and with the animals in which he was especially interested there was a sexual union of male and female, and how the body developed from this union was a matter that no one up to Von Baer's time had been able to find out.

There had been many guesses, for the hidden and mysterious development of life has always fascinated those who contemplate it.

Aristotle had considered it. He believed that flies and mice were generated from filth, to be sure, but he had watched the growth of the chick in a hen's egg. The first two books of his *Natural History* were written on this subject and illustrated with drawings.

In the Middle Ages a monk wrote that if you put some bran, some cheese, and some old rags in a corner, mice would be born from them. At that time it was not uncommon for people to believe that if a woman was put under a spell she might give birth to kittens or puppies.

William Harvey, whose great work was on the circulation of the blood, would, of course, have nothing to do with such notions. "All things come from the egg," he said in 1651. But he had never seen the egg of a mammal. He had merely made a shrewd guess.

The microscope helped more than anything else to solve the mystery of reproduction. But even with the microscope, understanding was slow in coming.

Malpighi, in the seventeenth century, had peered down at the tiny pulsating speck in a hen's egg and thought he could see in it a tiny chicken with heart and lungs, head, wings, and legs, all nicely folded. The only thing needed was some stimulus to make the egg hatch. At that time it was not even known that this must be a tangible thing; it might simply be a kind of immaterial impulse, invisible yet effective.

The idea that the embryo contained the perfect adult form in miniature was called "preformation." It led to great discussion. For what was true for a chicken would doubtless be true for any other living creature—a human being for instance. If the being inside the egg was complete in all its parts, then it must have an ovary and eggs of its own. And if such eggs were there, they in turn must contain other complete beings. So they would all be folded, one inside the other, tinier and tinier, down to the most minute little creature imaginable. If that was true, it was said that Eve, the first woman, must have had inside her body the minute forms of all the men and women that ever were to be—and every one of them complete, with head and arms and legs. One writer estimated that the number of them might be twenty-seven million!

In 1679 Leeuwenhoek made a great discovery. He saw through the lens of his microscope some little, moving organisms with whipping tails, which he later identified as spermatozoa. It was because he had the theory of preformation clearly in his mind that he said he could see the form of a little man in the sperm.

As time went on, the botanists talked of male and female in the growth of plants, and they talked of preformation in these too. They imagined the complete bean vines neatly folded inside the bean, the oak trees inside the acorn. All plants seemed to them to be like the paper flowers the Japanese so cleverly insert in capsules, which spread out when they are dropped into a glass of water.

Not all the scientists believed in preformation. As the seventeenth century passed into the eighteenth, and the eighteenth into the nineteenth, more and more of them believed that living things were created in another way. They talked of "epigenesis," and by that term they meant that the simplest form becomes progressively more complex as it grows—that the egg changes somehow into the embryo, that the embryo develops and grows until it becomes a plant, a fish, a rabbit, or a human being.

This was the state of things when Karl Ernst von Baer began his embryological work. He was a German who had been born in Estonia, on the Baltic Sea. He had studied at various German universities, and, because his friend Christian Heinrich Pander was teaching at the University of Saint Petersburg in Russia, he too obtained a professor's post at that university. Up to the time Von Baer started his researches, no one had ever seen the ovum, or egg, of a mammal. Eggs of birds, fish, and reptiles were common enough, and theoretically everyone agreed that there must be such a thing as a mammalian ovum. So Von Baer began at the very beginning. He searched for the egg of a mammal.

Von Baer did not use a microscope, although his eyes were not very good. He started by dissecting a great many different kinds of mammals. After he had searched a long time, he found what he was looking for. He found it in the ovary of a rabbit—a tiny gray speck, yet big enough to see with his naked eye. So that was it!

But he was not content with finding only one. He went on with his search. There was, he discovered, an ovum in the ovary of a dog. And finally he was satisfied, but not surprised, to find one in the body of a human being.

So he had proved that mammals, though they give birth to their young in living form (the biologists talk of mammals as "viviparous"), nevertheless emerge, as Harvey had said, from an egg. Here was another proof of the unity of all living things: the seeds of plants; the eggs of fish, reptiles, and birds; the ova of mammals.

But how, Von Baer asked next, is it possible for this tiny speck I have seen to grow into an embryo? What happens?

With this problem his friend Christian Heinrich Pander was able to help him. Pander too had been fascinated by the problem of how a fertilized egg develops into an embryo, and had worked out a theory—a theory which biologists still hold today. After the egg has been fertilized, said Pander, it divides into two parts; the two parts divide into four; the four into sixteen; and so on. Finally they form themselves into a hollow sphere called the *blastula*. The blastula then grows longitudinally. The walls approach each other and become flattened. And then a third, middle layer grows between the upper and the lower one. The three layers now lie one on top of the other. Pander called them *Blätter,* the German word for leaves. Since these leaves, or layers, are the germ of new life, he also called them germ layers.

Now, as the germ layers grow they start to curl inward and fold themselves. And as a piece of paper might be folded by a child to make a little boat or a hat, so the germ layers are folded to make up the various parts of the body. One folds itself around until it makes a tube, which will hold the embryo. In this, another folds itself to make the alimentary canal and vital organs; another makes the bony frame or skeleton; and another the skin. So the tiny germinal leaves curl and stretch, fold themselves and grow, until the complete embryo is formed.

In his laboratory at Saint Petersburg Von Baer collected a large number of embryos, and, putting them in alcohol, set the glass jars in rows on the shelves of his laboratory. Each one was carefully labeled.

As the collection grew he became more and more interested in seeing that in the earliest stages of their development all the embryos looked much alike. He wrote, "Are not all animals in the beginning of their development essentially alike, and is there not a primary form common to all?"

Still, though it was evident to him that the embryonic forms were all somehow related, he could never accept the theory of evolution.

Darwin, however, was greatly interested in the following passage in Von Baer's writings:

"The embryos of mammalia, of birds, lizards, and snakes, are, in their earliest states, exceedingly like one another, both as a whole and in the mode of development of their parts; indeed, we can often distinguish such embryos only by their size. I have two little embryos in spirit to which I have omitted to attach the names. I am now quite unable to say to what class they belong. They may be lizards, or small birds, or very young mammals, so complete is the similarity of the mode of development of the head and trunk in these animals. The extremities are still absent, but even if present we should learn nothing from them in this early stage of development, for the feet of lizards and mammals, the wings and feet of birds, no less than the hands and feet of men, originate in the same fundamental plan."

As he worked, observing his embryos, it appeared that sometimes organs developed and disappeared again. Thus every embryo after about twenty days had the gill slits of a fish, but in most animals these slits disappeared before the embryo was more than a few weeks old. In all the animals there seemed to have been a tail, but in men this disappeared before birth. In human beings, however, some organs, such as the appendix, were preserved although their function was not understood.

Ernst Haeckel, who was Darwin's great admirer in Germany, thought the stages through which the individual embryo passes are a recapitulation of the history of the race. He wrote: "The individual repeats during the rapid and short course of its development the most important of the form changes which its ancestors traversed during the long and slow course of their paleontological evolution."

Most modern biologists do not believe that this is true, although the theory is often repeated.

The work that Von Baer did with his embryos is, however, another matter. His discovery of the mammalian ova, his brilliant conception of the germ plasm, his proof of the likeness of men and animals in their early stages—these are the foundation stones on which modern embryologists work.

XIV. SCHLEIDEN AND SCHWANN
AGREE ON A THEORY

A GENTLE, quiet man, full of good will and kindliness; a man who avoided arguments and wanted only to keep on with his research—that was Theodor Schwann. He worked at the Anatomical Institute in Berlin in the middle of the nineteenth century. And he was the last man in the world to stir up controversy or to want change, yet his discoveries, coupled with those of his friend Matthias Schleiden, roused arguments that resounded in every part of the scientific world. Their theory has been the basis of biological thought ever since.

Schwann and Schleiden together worked out what is known as the cell theory. Schwann, the physiologist, should perhaps be given more credit for the theory, but Schleiden, the botanist, contributed. Because of their work, men first understood Von Baer's germ layers, and the stuff from which the tissues of animal bodies are made, and the substances of plants and tree trunks. They pointed out, in fact, the material structure of the whole living world. Their theory was all-embracing and all-inclusive in its scope.

Yet they were simple men, both of them—Schwann a little phlegmatic perhaps; Schleiden more impatient and volatile.

We are fortunate that one of Schwann's friends, named Henle, has left a description of him. He wrote: "He was a man of stature below the medium, with a beardless face, an almost infantile and always-smiling expression, smooth, dark brown hair, wearing a fur-trimmed dressing gown, living in a poorly lighted room on the second floor of a restaurant which was not even second class. He would pass whole days there without going out, with a few rare books around him, and numerous glass vessels, retorts, vials, and tubes, simple apparatus which he made himself. . . .

"Or I go in imagination to the dark fusty halls of the Anatomical Institute, where we used to work till nightfall by the side of our excellent chief, Johannes Müller," Henle goes on to say. "We took our dinner in the evening, after the English fashion, so that we might enjoy more of the advantages of the daylight. Our porter's wife furnished the meat, we the wine and wit. Those were happy days when the first good microscopes had been sent out from the shops of Plössi at Vienna, or of Pistor and Schick at Berlin, which we paid for by exercising a student's economies; happy days when it was still possible to make a first-class discovery by scraping an animal membrane with the nail or cutting it with the scalpel."

The group of men who were working in the "dark fusty halls of the Anatomical Institute" in Berlin were assistants of the famed physiologist Johannes Müller. Müller was writing an ambitious textbook on physiology, which, he planned, should contain no statement that either he or his assistants had not demonstrated to be true.

Now, for the first time since the seventeenth century, great improvements had been made in the manufacture of microscopes. And this meant that scientific workers could see a great many things which even such intrepid explorers as Malpighi, Swammerdam, and Leeuwenhoek had been unable to observe. So Johannes Müller's assistants who saved their money to get fine instruments from the new microscope companies made a great many discoveries.

Theodor Schwann was one of the most eager and the most methodical of the group. A native of Rhenish Prussia, he had come to the Institute after long, thorough training at the universities of Bonn, Cologne, and Würzburg. He had also received a medical degree from the University of Berlin. As he worked under Johannes Müller he began almost at once to find out what had been unknown before. He showed how certain organisms and lower fungi could produce fermentation and putrefaction, and this paved the way for the germ theory of Pasteur. He proved at the same time that the idea of spontaneous generation was impossible. And he found out that a certain ferment, which he called *pepsin*, was necessary to digestion.

All these are undisputed facts now, but to Theodor Schwann and his friends the discovery was a great adventure. The work that was most revolutionary, however, and which made the name of the amiable Theodor Schwann great above those of his fellow workers at the Institute, was his work on cells.

Peering down through his microscope, as many others had done before him, he examined the minute structure of the tissues under the lens and made deductions that set the world of biology on a new basis.

The idea of cells was not an original one with Schwann. Back in the seventeenth century Robert Hooke, in England, had examined a thin slice of cork and had said it was composed of minute "cells." They reminded him of the cells in a honeycomb. Here and there scientists had occasionally noticed them. But none of them realized the universality of cells, or thought very much about them—none of them till Theodor Schwann.

Could it be that all animal tissues, all organs, bones, skin, are composed of cells? he asked himself. Are they like tiny building blocks of which all animal substances are made? He looked again. "Incredible!" he said; yet since he had seen it, he believed it. Could it be that every single cell is exactly like every other, the only difference, then, being in their arrangement?

He checked his findings and checked again. He could see no reason for thinking he was wrong. He had been trained in thorough German fashion to make no deduction until he had examined a large number of cases. For many days he examined his specimens. He found no deviation from the general rule. Every animal substance appeared to be built up of cells like little building blocks, and all the cells were alike.

Then another idea came to him. Was it possible that not animal tissues only, but the tissues of all living things, were composed of cells—trees and plants, fungi and mushrooms, and everything else that had life in it? Were the cells the same as those that composed the animal tissues?

It would take a botanist to determine that. He had a friend who was a botanist, Matthias Schleiden. He would invite him to dinner.

So we introduce Matthias Schleiden. He has been called "one of the strangest personalities of his age"—a moody, despondent man, but brilliant. He had originally planned to be a barrister and had received his law degree with high honors. But, when he started to practice law in his native Hamburg, he had no success in pleading cases, and this threw him into such despair that he tried to shoot himself. The bullet missed its mark, and he lived, but that was the end of his legal career.

Now he decided he would study natural science, and soon he had won degrees in both philosophy and medicine. Botany was the branch that interested him most. Before long he was writing brilliant books on botany.

They were hastily written and sometimes inaccurate, but they attracted much attention. He was thirty-three years old, and had already published an important work on plant cells, when Theodor Schwann invited him to dinner.

It is not recorded whether the restaurant in which the two scientists met was the one below Schwann's room described as "not even second class," but it does not matter.

They talked. The amiable Schwann described the cells that he had seen in animal tissues. Was it possible that the cells in plants, which Schleiden had described, were like them?

Schleiden must have listened with some excitement. They sat late, talking over their coffee and cigars. Finally they left the restaurant and went to Schwann's room. There Schwann took out his microscope, and together they examined plant and animal tissues, till there was no doubt in the mind of either of them.

It was Schwann who announced the cell theory. In 1838 he published an article in a German scientific periodical, and later he announced it to the French Academy of Sciences. In 1839 he followed these papers with a treatise, *Microscopic Investigations on the Accordance in the Structure and Growth of Plants and Animals*. The book contains two hundred and fifteen pages and is illustrated with four plates. It is one of biology's great works.

In it Schwann wrote: "The elementary parts of all tissues are formed of cells in an analogous though very diversified manner, so that it may be asserted that there is one universal principle of development for the elementary parts of organisms however different, and that this principle is the formation of cells."

Now it was clear that many riddles which had hitherto been insolvable could be solved. The germinal layers, for instance, whose growth and folding Von Baer had not been able to explain, grew because new cells were added and arranged in a particular way. The ovum and the sperm were modified cells. With their union, new cells were added till the embryo of plant or animal was made.

The cell theory has been called a "master stroke of generalization." It has been said that it was "one of the greatest discoveries of the nineteenth century." But the scientists of the nineteenth century were by no means agreed in their belief in it. The controversy that Schwann and Schleiden stirred up continued for twenty years. Some scientists said that the two men had insufficient proof for their assertions. They pointed to the fact that Schleiden had made some errors in his book on botany, for Schleiden was indeed too hasty in his work. No one could say that of Schwann.

The manner in which the two men met this uproar of disapproval was characteristic. Schleiden, who lacked Schwann's self-control, was quick to enter controversies. He took up every battle, indulging in argument and

personal vituperation. Finally he grew so indignant that he
gave up botany altogether and turned his attention to
anthropology. When he died he was working on a paper
to which he had given the title, "Salt, the Rose, the Horse,
as Agents of Civilization."

To Theodor Schwann, on the other hand, all the alterca-
tions made little difference. Quietly, hardly noticing what
people said of him, he continued with his work. Those
cells—he wanted to know more about them. There was so
much he had not yet found out. But one man can do only
so much in his lifetime, and the little units of which life
is built are complex structures.

Later biologists have corroborated the work that
Schwann and Schleiden did. All terrestrial life is cell life,
they say. No other kind exists. Every plant, from the tiniest
alga to the giant redwood tree, every animal, from the
microbe to the whale or the elephant, is composed of cells.
The biologists have measured them. The average cell is
0.0008 inches long, they say. It would take two billion
cells to fill a cubic inch!

But if these tiny units are the elements of which all
living things are built, what are they made of? This was
a problem that Schwann and Schleiden did not succeed in
solving.

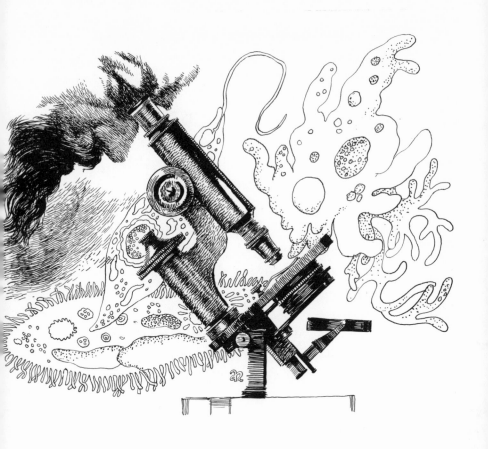

XV. THE STUFF OF LIFE

IN 1861, while the controversies about the cell theory
were raging, Max Schultze, the German zoologist,
began to examine cells through his microscope. Before long
he had his own statement to make about them. He said a
cell was "a mass of protoplasm provided with a nucleus."

And what was a mass of protoplasm? And what was a nucleus? In about two years he had a pretty good idea of the answers to these questions; and at this time he followed his first statement with another. "Protoplasm is the physical basis of life," he said.

Many scientists before Schultze's time had noticed the sap or jelly-like substance that was to be found in animals and plants. Probably Johannes Purkinje of Prague was the first of these. He found it in plants but did not understand what it was. He was a devout Christian, and decided to call it *protoplasm*, taking the name from Protoplastus, which, in the liturgy of the Church, was another name for Adam.

Hugo von Mohl, the German botanist, had seen through his microscope the same substance in the slime-like, granule-filled material that traveled with a circular movement within plant cells.

And then Félix Dujardin, studying the single-celled marine creatures called protozoa, noticed it too. He said it was "a substance, viscid, translucent, homogenous, elastic, and contractile." He called it *sarcode*.

But though all these men had seen the jelly-like substance in animals and in plants, none of them attached great importance to it, having perhaps set their eyes on other matters.

Then, while the scientific world was arguing about the cells that Schleiden and Schwann had talked of, Max

Schultze asked his question and gave his answer. At first little attention was paid to him. But gradually the biologists began to realize the importance of what he had said. By the time the twentieth century had come, they believed that the study of the cell with its protoplasm and nucleus might give them the key to understanding life itself.

It is a pity that more has not been written about Max Schultze. We know that his life was short: he died at forty-nine. We know that he was a lecturer at the university at Halle in Prussia, and a professor at the University of Bonn. We know that he loved music: he kept his violin close beside his microscope. And we have his picture, the picture of an intellectual, sensitive man wearing a dark suit and a bow tie, and with a straggly beard.

Perhaps he would prefer that the details of his personal life not be recorded. Certainly he would feel that his work was more important, and there is plenty of information about this.

In his laboratory at the University of Bonn he was known as a hard worker, particularly when it came to his microscope. Soon he was famous for his studies of amoebas, the little single-celled animals that look like tiny globules of jelly moving through sea water. He studied the ramifications of the nervous system in vertebrates too, and made important contributions to the knowledge of electricity in animal bodies. But his great contributions grew from his study of the amoeba.

For he realized that these little globules of jelly-like stuff were in fact living creatures. They had the power to move from one place to another, changing their shapes to form little "false foots," and then, after they had moved, drawing them back again. When he touched them or passed a slight current of electricity through them they changed their form. He saw, moreover, that they seemed to consume nourishment and excrete waste, and that they took in oxygen and gave out carbon dioxide. And since they also had the power to reproduce by dividing themselves into two parts, he knew that they were animals.

Looking down through his lens, Max Schultze saw the stuff of which the amoeba was made. It was a mass of jelly containing a nucleus. The jelly sometimes grew cloudy, sometimes was clear. There was movement in it. Sometimes it seemed to be a whirling movement, sometimes a hardly perceptible drift. Others had seen this movement before him. Robert Brown had seen it first, and so scientists called it the Brownian movement. They did not know what it was.

Max Schultze began to examine the jelly-like substance in other animals and in plants. In animals the movement seemed to be rather slow, but in plants it went whirling around at a great rate. Strange, he must have thought, for we have thought of plants as stationary and animals as moving. He could not understand it, but he knew that the movement in the protoplasm was the movement of life. When the cells died, the movement stopped.

In 1861 he was ready to publish his findings in a short and rather unassuming essay, which he sent to the German *Journal of Anatomy and Physiology*.

In the beginning of this essay he made the statement that a cell was a mass of protoplasm containing a nucleus. And he went on to say that it would be impossible for a cell to have surrounding walls. If it had walls, how could it divide in two? And if it could not divide in two, how could it reproduce? It would be like an imprisoned animal.

It ought not to be called a cell at all, he reasoned. For it is almost impossible to think of a cell without walls. The cell of a honeycomb has walls of wax; a monk's cell or a prison cell—both are spaces surrounded by walls. Still, since biologists had spoken of cells for so long, he did not suggest altering the name. Yet, he declared, the cells of which all living things are made are simply infinitesimal masses of jelly-like protoplasm, each with its nucleus. Of course, he said, they have no walls.

Moreover, he said, the protoplasm that surrounds the nuclei in different tissues differs not because of any substance foreign to the cell; its different forms are simply a transformation of the protoplasm itself. The very name, protoplasm, which formerly had been used only by botanists, should be the universal term for the substance that is fundamental to all life. It is found in plants, in lower animals and higher animals. Its consistency is different in different animals and kinds of plants. Sometimes a number of nuclei can be surrounded by this protoplasm, which can afterward separate and form separate cells.

That was the substance of the essay Max Schultze published. Since then microscopes have been greatly improved —now they can magnify up to four and five hundred times—and biologists have found out more about the protoplasm that is the stuff of life.

Protoplasm is a substance which scientists call a colloid. It resembles glue or white of egg. More than eighty per cent of it is water, and in this water float tiny particles, or granules, which combine and recombine, break apart and drift together again. It lives by change. At times the protoplasm appears perfectly clear under a high-powered microscope. At other times it is grayish and again there are tiny particles floating in it.

Most of the changes cannot be seen even through the sharpest of lenses, but as the tiny particles shift, join into new combinations, and separate again, the whole colloidal system changes, producing movement, growth, and other vital functions. Living, therefore, is the sum of all the changes that take place in the protoplasm.

As they watch the changes and the movements in the living cells, scientists have sought to find out what protoplasm is made of. Can it be made from the materials that are found on earth, or is there some special essence, some peculiar force in it that does not belong to the material of earth? Does protoplasm have any elements in it that are not already on the earth?

Here chemists have come to the aid of biologists in the important new branch of science known as biochemistry. Though their study is still in its beginnings, this is what they have found.

Every kind of protoplasm contains nine elements. These are oxygen, carbon, hydrogen, nitrogen, potassium, phosphorus, sulphur, magnesium, and iron. All these are plentiful on the surface of the earth. Some kinds of protoplasm contain additional elements. Calcium, sodium, chlorine, and copper have been found in them. But these are common earth elements too. Therefore, up to the present time the biochemists have found nothing to make them believe that protoplasm contains any substance that is not contained in water, air, and the rocks of the earth.

How these material substances combine, why they react as they do, whether it would ever be possible for a scientist to combine them and to create life—these are unsolved questions.

But even as we ask them, the wonder and the mystery of life remain. What is it? What is this protoplasm, this elemental jelly that Max Schultze found in all living things? What is the stuff of the oak tree digging its roots into the ground, the daisy blowing in the wind, the boy running across the field?

They are mysteries now as they were before high-powered microscopes were ever invented.

Thomas Huxley, the nineteenth-century English scientist, made a singular description of protoplasm as seen through a microscope. Incidentally, he had been a surgeon on the British ship, H. M. S. *Rattlesnake*, where he had made a serious study of the surface life of the tropical seas. Concerning his findings, he sent back "communication after communication to the Linnaean Society." When *The Origin of Species* was published, he found in it a good working hypothesis for evolution.

Having examined the cell of a plant through a microscope, Huxley wrote: "The spectacle afforded by the wonderful energies imprisoned within the compass of the microscopic cell of a plant, which we commonly regard as a merely passive organism, is not easily forgotten by one who has watched its movement hour by hour without pause or sign of weakening.

"The possible complexity of many other organisms seemingly as simple as the protoplasm of the plant just mentioned dawns on one, and the comparison of such activity to that of higher animals loses much of its startling character. Currents similar to these have been observed in a great multitude of different plants, and it is uniformly believed that they occur in more or less perfection in all young vegetable cells. If such be the case, the wonderful noonday silence of a tropical forest is due, after all, only to the dullness of our hearing, and could our ears catch the murmur of these tiny maelstroms as they whirl in the innumerable myriads of living cells that constitute each tree, we should be stunned, as with the roar of a great city."

XVI. PEA VINES AND MATHEMATICS

EARLY on a summer morning in 1860 Gregor Mendel, in his long monk's habit, pushed open the door of the white-walled monastery of Altbrünn in Austria and walked along a gravel path to a small vegetable patch neatly planted with pea vines. The red edge of the sun was just pushing up over the Austrian hills; trees and shrubs in the quiet monastery grounds were beginning to take shape. No one stirred. Even the birds sounded sleepy.

Gregor Mendel walked quickly. The pea vines were in flower, and he wanted to reach them before the bees started to carry pollen from one to another.

He shut the gate of the vegetable garden behind him and started to work. He was very fat, and his monk's habit interfered with his movements. But his hands were skillful: he had worked in exactly this way every summer for nearly eleven years.

The red and white peas were in full flower. The vines had been trained up on strings, and some of them were supported on twigs or short poles. With a little brush

Mendel took the pollen from a red pea blossom and dusted it carefully on the pistil of a white pea. Then he tied a bag over the flower he had fertilized in this way, and moved over to the next flower. The patch measured about 20 feet by 120, so the work was tedious. It was mid-morning before he had finished his curious task.

Gregor Mendel was used to working with growing things. He had been born in the country, the son of poor Austrian peasants. But it was early evident that he had a quick mind. The master at the village school noticed that he was particularly good at mathematics. So somehow, though they had little money, his parents managed to send him to a higher school twenty miles away, and worried because they could not pay full board. They sent him "bread and butter" from home every time the carrier went that way.

After he had finished school the boy entered the monastery at Altbrünn, and there, according to monastic custom, he chose a new name. His parents had christened him Johann; now he was to be Gregor.

The superiors at the monastery recognized too that the boy had a quick mind. They sent him to the University of Vienna for three years. After that he came back to the monastery to teach and to make the experiments with beans and peas that interested him so much.

For though the prelate of the monastery had said that Gregor Mendel "lived blamelessly, piously, and religiously," and though he was a good teacher, who explained things simply to his pupils, he cared above everything else for the experiments he was making with his beans and peas. He had worked at them for nearly eleven years, and by the summer of 1860 his experiments were nearly completed. He felt that he had solved a great mystery, that he had discovered a natural law whose existence no one had guessed before. Soon he would be ready to tell the world about it. Standing in his monk's garb with his pea blossoms carefully tied up, each in its little bag, he must have smiled to himself before he went back through the great door to his other duties in the monastery.

The problem on which he had been working was a hard one. No one who did not have an observing eye and a good mind for mathematics would have tried it. But Gregor Mendel had both.

He was studying heredity. Whatever he could prove from watching bean and pea vines would be true of other living plants and animals, he thought. He knew, as did all scientists in his day, that in the living world like tends to produce like, that the offspring of plants as well as of animals tend to be like their parents. He knew that the only substances that passed from one generation to another were the microscopic egg and sperm in animals and their equivalent in plants, except for the single-celled animals, which reproduce by dividing, or the plants that increase by budding. But how this thread of life was carried down from one generation to another, whether a human being inherited his qualities equally from both parents, whether he inherited anything from his grandparents or from his remote ancestors—these were things he did not know. He thought he could find them out through his work with the pea blossoms in the garden patch.

It had been a long time since the idea had first come to him. He had always been interested in gardening, and in his early years at the monastery he had tried to produce new colors in his flowers. Soon he noticed that the flowers called hybrids, which were a mixture of two stocks, kept producing certain colors with extraordinary regularity. He would make a chart of these hybrids and their offspring, he thought. It seemed strange that no one had thought of doing this before. Perhaps in this way he could explain the great variety of species in plants and animals.

After Mendel had experimented with more than two thousand pea vines, he was ready to put the natural law that he had discovered into words. When he crossed red flowers with white flowers the hybrids were uniformly red. In the next generation, however, when the hybrids were crossed with one another, the new generation produced was mixed. Of every four plants, on the average, three had red blossoms and one had white blossoms.

The red color he called the *dominant* characteristic, the white the *recessive*. Now he experimented with other characteristics: with peas whose skins were wrinkled and smooth; those with tall vines or short; those whose seed coats were white, grayish, brown, or yellow. Always the dominant and recessive characteristics appeared in the same proportions.

He saw now that inheritance was not a matter of blending; that the reproductive cells were a little mosaic, bearing characteristic qualities of both parent plants or animals. And he could predict in advance exactly the kind and proportion of the members of each new generation— an ability that was to be very valuable to animal-breeders and plant-growers in the future.

In 1864, in a fine copperplate hand, he wrote a brief paper explaining the phenomenon of inheritance he had discovered.

There was a meeting of the Brünn Society for the Study of Natural Science in February, 1865. Gregor Mendel was invited to read his paper to its members. Although the night was extremely cold, a few members turned out. Among them were botanists, a chemist, a geologist, and an astronomer. They listened politely enough to the account of his work with the pea vines, though it is questionable whether what he said was very clear to them. There was not time for him to finish. He would complete his paper, with special attention to his mathematical calculations, at the March meeting, he said.

Scarcely anyone attended the March meeting. Those who did come hardly followed the argument at all. Botany and mathematics were an unheard-of combination, they said.

It was the custom of the Brünn Society to send copies of its proceedings to other scientific societies. Copies of Mendel's paper were, therefore, duly made and sent to Vienna, Berlin, Rome, Saint Petersburg, and Uppsala. But no one paid any attention to them. Perhaps they were not even read. A monk with a theory of heredity completely at variance with the prevailing thought of the day? A monk who mingled botany with mathematics? Why should anyone pay heed to him?

Yet Gregor Mendel felt sure that what he had discovered was important. A year or two later he was writing to Karl Wilhelm Nägeli, the renowned Swiss botanist. Would Nägeli care to see a little paper he had written, he asked. Nägeli was bad-tempered and in poor health, but he agreed to read Mendel's paper. Afterward he wrote Mendel that the monk seemed to have "made a beginning."

Mendel still believed in the discovery he had made. He went on with his experiments, working with hybrids of four-o'clocks and of maize, with dandelions and with hawkweed. The monastery disapproved of his working with animal specimens.

As he grew older the work grew increasingly difficult because of his corpulence. And with the dandelions and the four-o'clocks he needed to use a microscope, which caused him severe eyestrain. Nevertheless, he planned to continue in spite of bodily difficulties and lack of recognition.

But in 1868 he was chosen to be head of the monastery at Altbrünn. He took the post with regret. He wanted to go on with his teaching and his work in heredity. Perhaps, he thought, he would be able to devote a larger part of the monastery grounds to his experiments. He wanted too to experiment with honeybees and fruit trees.

But in less than six years he fell into a bitter struggle with the German government. They wanted to tax the monastery, and Mendel maintained they had no right to do so. For several years he tried to fight the government, and this took so much time and strength that his scientific studies had to be set aside.

He died at the monastery in 1884. A great crowd of mourners came to his funeral. They were not only the priests and the monks, but a Protestant clergyman, the Jewish rabbi of Altbrünn, representatives of the scientific society, professors, teachers, and townspeople. They mourned him with genuine grief, for they had loved him, but no one at that time seemed to realize that they were burying the body of a great scientist on whose discoveries students of heredity would base their work for generations to come. They thought of him simply as a good man.

The years passed. In 1900, in laboratories in three separate countries, three scientists, working separately, came to the same conclusion. Hugo De Vries the Dutchman,

Karl Correns the German, and Tschermak the Austrian all pointed out that their findings corroborated exactly what Mendel had discovered years before.

Now the world awoke slowly to the importance of Gregor Mendel's work. The townspeople of Altbrünn collected money in 1911 to erect a marble statue to him. On it he stands in his monk's habit, the beans and pea vines around him; and underneath is the inscription:

TO THE INVESTIGATOR OF NATURE

P. GREGOR MENDEL

1822–1884

Under this inscription in low relief are the figures of a man and a woman kneeling with joined hands. They are intended to show the importance that the old monk's work will have to the human life of future generations.

XVII. PRIMROSES IN A POTATO FIELD

TOWARD the end of the nineteenth century, while some scientists were tracing the growth of embryos or looking through their microscopes at minute cells and others were examining the movements within a speck of protoplasm, a great many biologists were identifying new species of animals and plants. That absorbing occupation, which Linnaeus had begun, now reached huge proportions.

Soon it appeared that the diversity of living forms on the earth was far greater than anyone had imagined. Millions of different animals were studied and named. The scientists found more than two hundred thousand species of plants, and still they kept finding more. Probably there were twice as many animals and plants as those they had accounted for, they said.

Besides all the various living species, they found the fossil remains of many that had once lived and disappeared again. Bones of strange, unknown animals were unearthed from clay pits and sandbanks. Traces of ancient ferns remained in strata of rocks, and tree trunks millions of years old were pressed down into the earth in petrified form. Some of these plants and animals appeared to be related to living species; some of them were entirely different in every way, as if they had lived but left no descendants.

How did so many different species start? the biologists kept asking. It was a very old question indeed.

Lamarck had thought that as each animal or plant adapted itself to its environment it acquired new characteristics which it passed on to later generations. So finally a new species of animal was developed.

Darwin had found another explanation for the creation of new species. He thought that in the struggle for existence nature selected those that were best fitted to live.

In this way small variations that were of advantage to the living creature were preserved, and these were accentuated from one generation to another, until a new species was formed. It would take thousands of years to bring such a thing about, he acknowledged, but the earth had been inhabited for thousands of years, and he could see no other possible explanation.

In whatever way the various species were made in the first place, it was certainly true that millions of them could live side by side and never intermingle. A dog did not mate with a cat, nor a skunk with a raccoon. Oak and ash, beech and maple, remained separate from each other. Even the insects, of which there are so many million kinds, did not usually cross the line. One man counted 1402 different species of insects in his back yard!

Rarely the lines of species did cross, and a creature mated outside its own group, but then the offspring, called hybrids, could generally not reproduce again. Why was all this? No one had been able to find out.

Mendel, the Augustinian monk, had done more work on the question of heredity than anyone else. But he did not know why characteristics were passed on in a particular way, and he did not know how new species were created. Nature guarded her mystery closely. And then came Hugo De Vries, trying to wrest her secret from her.

Hugo De Vries was professor of botany at the University

of Amsterdam and director of the Botanic Garden there. He was handsome, with a thin face, a pointed beard, and an expression at once penetrating, lively, and sympathetic.

He was endowed also with a great gift of patience. "Assiduity and exactitude" were needed, he said, for the work in which he was engaged.

Hugo De Vries set to work first with marigolds, working in the Botanic Garden in Amsterdam. He counted the florets on thousands of the plants, collecting and labeling them to try to find out the laws by which some of the little golden flowers inherited their colors and forms from the generation that had gone before, while others appeared to have quite different characteristics.

For although De Vries was a follower of Darwin, he had observed that plant-growers and animal-breeders made little progress by selecting for reproduction the reddest roses or the race horses with the strongest muscles. They waited, instead, for a particular trait to crop out, and seized upon it. Nägeli, the botanist who had paid so little attention to Gregor Mendel, had suggested that new species originated in sudden changes, in *sports*, or what he called *mutations*. And De Vries was inclined to believe that this was true.

How could he prove it? Not in the Botanic Garden, it seemed. All his counting of marigold florets came to nothing. Perhaps he could find some other plants to work on, he thought. Perhaps he could see the thing better if he studied wild flowers.

He began to search the country around Amsterdam for examples of the plants he wanted to study. He considered and rejected nearly a hundred different kinds of plants. Then one day he came upon an abandoned potato field. The owner of the potato field, Dr. Juris Six, did not value it much. It was bordered on two sides by canals, and no road led into it. That was why he had been unable to rent it for potato-growing. It had lain fallow for several years, and wild plants had grown up in it undisturbed.

De Vries came to the field for the first time toward evening, and as he approached it he saw a great mass of yellow primroses, tall as a man's head. They had escaped from a neighboring park and multiplied, and here they were, glowing in the evening light. As he walked closer, he said, he was impressed by their "stately beauty," their tall stems crowned with yellow flowers over which butterflies and bumblebees were hovering. Here were the subjects for his study.

De Vries knew a great deal about primroses already. He knew there were many species but that they were all called *Oenothera*. He knew that they were originally American plants, and that one species had been taken from Virginia to Europe in 1614. Two other species had been imported to Europe in the eighteenth century. The species in the potato field was called *Oenothera Lamarckiana,* for

Lamarck had first identified them among the plants growing in the garden of the Museum of Natural History in
Paris.

Standing in the abandoned potato field, De Vries examined the plants before him. There were great differences
in the height of the plants, the form of the leaves, the way
the stems branched. He knew almost at once that this was
the place where, if he was sufficiently patient, he could
find out what he wanted to know.

"Here was a wonderful opportunity of getting an insight
into the phenomenon of variation as exhibited by a plant
that was multiplying rapidly," he wrote later.

In 1886 he took a house at a short distance from the
field, and almost every day that year he spent several
hours studying his evening primroses.

In the summer of 1887, in a corner of the field, he found
ten specimens that he knew immediately were a new type:
their petals were small and oval and quite different from
those of the other plants. He called them *Oenothera
laevifolia.*

He worked on, examining the seedlings, observing
leaves and stems and flowers. By the end of 1889 he had
examined 53,509 plants in eight generations, and among
them he had discovered eight completely new types. He
cross-pollinated them, and every time they bred true.

Later he wrote of the new species: "They came into
existence at once, fully equipped, without preparation or

intermediate steps. No series of generations, no selection, no struggle for existence, was needed. It was a sudden leap into a new type, a *sport* in the best accepted tradition of the word. It fulfilled my hopes, and at once gave proof of the possibility of direct observation of the origin of species and of the experimental control thereof."

When De Vries first announced his mutation theory it was met with a storm of protest. He had not performed his experiments carefully enough, the biologists said. Was he pretending that he could supplant Darwin's theory of the survival of the fittest?

But the friends of De Vries saw in his work a great advance over the old theorizing. Certainly Darwin's idea of the survival of the fittest still holds good, they said. But De Vries' mutations supply new characters which may or may not survive. People have talked of mutations before, they said. De Vries has proved that they exist.

But though De Vries established the fact that mutations exist, they are still not very well understood. They must not be considered miracles. If they seem to be exceptions to general laws, it may be that this is only because we do not fully understand the general laws. "The understanding must be stretched and enlarged to take in the image of the universe as it is discovered," Francis Bacon said in the sixteenth century, and this seems still to be true.

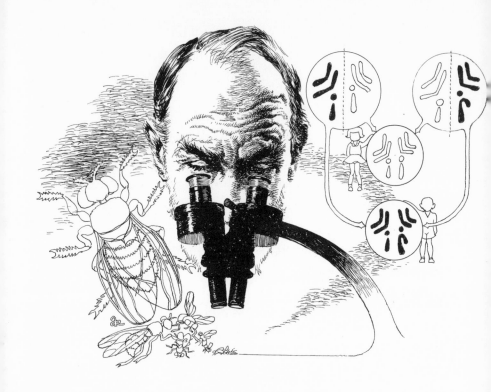

XVIII. WE ARE
STILL AT THE BEGINNING

SO, STEP by step, the great biologists worked, examining the strange phenomena of birth and life and death. And still there were unsolved problems and mysteries they could not understand. Though they had worked with the brilliance of Aristotle, and watched the "marvels of nature" with the wonder of Marcello Malpighi, though they had studied patiently, as William Harvey had

174

studied, there was much that was not yet understood.

August Weismann, working in his laboratory at the University of Freiburg in Germany, knew this. And he wanted to add what he could to the work of the biologists who had preceded him. He was particularly interested in heredity. What exactly is it that is passed down from one generation to the next? he asked himself. Why is the son generally like the father?

Weismann had been well trained for scientific work. For twenty-three years he had studied cell structure at German universities, and he had made some original contributions toward understanding it. But after that he found, as Malpighi and many others had discovered before him, that work with the microscope puts a great strain on the eyes. In time he developed glaucoma, a disease of the eye characterized by increased pressure within the eyeball and progressive loss of vision. For ten years he could not use his eyes at all. During those years, he says in his autobiography, he listened to music and listened while his wife read aloud to him. Finally his eyes improved: he was able to go on with his work.

He lived and worked till 1914. By that time he was a white-bearded old man who wore very thick spectacles. The questioning look that had been characteristic of his younger days was gone. He thought he had found the answer to a part, at least, of the problem he had been trying to solve.

"The reason the offspring tends to be like the parent," he said, "is that it is made of the same stuff. The cells of the body live and die again but among them there is one that is indestructible. It is the germ cell. It carries life from one generation to the next, and in this sense it is immortal."

Then he explained it further. He said in substance: "When the sperm unites with the ovum to create a new organism, the germ cell is passed down from one generation to another. The body cells develop only to nourish and protect these ageless bits of life.

"The germ cell is a specific substance," he went on. "It has a definite chemical and molecular structure. This is the bearer of heredity. It has passed down through the ages, bringing with it the accumulated characteristics which the new individual inherits. In this sense the new creature is a chip of the old block."

Perhaps it was fortunate that Weismann lived when he did, for microscopes were being continually improved, so that cell structures it had been impossible to see at an earlier time were easily discernible. Moreover, the biologists had found ways of staining a part of a nucleus with a dye that had little effect on the fat, starch, and protein that comprised the main part of it. The part they could stain they called the *chromosome*, which is a Greek word meaning "color body."

When Weismann's theory of germinal continuity was

announced, therefore, scientists in Germany, Sweden, England, Russia, the United States, and other countries began to investigate the chromosomes, which were the bearers of heredity. They used great ingenuity and patience. As they studied the chromosomes they soon saw that they were not all exactly alike and that they changed from time to time. They assumed different shapes. Sometimes they looked like rough sections of yarn, sometimes they were curved like sausages; or they might be twisted into irregular Vs or Ws.

The scientists also found that each species has a fixed number of chromosomes. They made a list of them, as follows:

Shark, 36
Mouse, salamander, trout, lily, 24
Worm called *Sagitta*, 18
Some kinds of snails, ox, guinea pig, and man, 48
Grasshopper, 12
The crustacean called *Artemia*, 168
Gypsy moth, 62
Pea, 14
Sea urchin, 54
Three kinds of wheat, 14, 28, 42, respectively
Three kinds of fruit flies, 8, 10, 12, respectively

So the prying eyes of the biologists were seeing what men had never seen before. But there was more to be discovered.

Each separate species, they observed, had an even number of chromosomes. When male and female were about to unite, the number of chromosomes in egg and sperm were reduced to half the original number. So the multiplication of chromosomes in each species was controlled, and the new individual started life with the right number for its species. Why was this so? The scientists could not tell.

They knew, however, that the germ cells of living things were not a fused product. The chromosomes that passed the complex characteristics of the individuals down from one generation to the other were a mosaic of particles. These particles were submicroscopic, far too minute to be seen. Yet the biologists did not doubt their existence. Each particle, which might be strung, like a precious bead, on the fragile thread of the chromosome, must be a separate entity, perhaps differing chemically or in some other way from the rest, they believed.

Soon young biologists everywhere were finding out more about these minute particles that determine the character of life.

The most distinguished work in this field was soon under way in America. Thomas Hunt Morgan, working at Columbia University in New York, was perhaps the most successful experimenter, though many others did brilliant work. They all had the same purpose. They wanted to prove, if they could, that Mendel's law was universal; they wanted to find out what brought De Vries' mutations about. They wanted, in fact, to understand heredity.

At first Morgan had some difficulty in finding a good subject for his experiments. He tried mice, rats, and pigeons. For one reason or another they were unsatisfactory. Then he tried experiments with plant lice, and decided that they were unsatisfactory too. At last he heard of a man at Harvard who had been making some experiments with fruit flies.

Someone has said that the fruit fly, *Drosophila melanogaster*, must have been created especially so that Thomas Hunt Morgan could make experiments. It was the ideal subject for his study. The small insect measures only about a quarter of an inch in length. Most people have seen it often, hovering near overripe peaches, plums, pears, and other fruits. It completes its life cycle from egg to winged adult fly in about ten days, and its life span is about ninety days. It can supply the experimenter thirty generations in a year. It multiplies rapidly, so that it is possible to raise a thousand fruit flies in a milk bottle. It thrives on a diet of bits of banana or other fruit, and apparently has no objection to living in a laboratory. And, best of all, it has four very large chromosomes that are not hard to see with the microscope.

Morgan had some fruit flies sent to his laboratory. They multiplied, and soon he had thousands and thousands of them. He set them in carefully labeled bottles in rows along his shelves. That was in 1909.

Then he began to submit his specimens to all sorts of tests. He tried unusually high temperatures and unusually low temperatures; he kept them in the dark and treated them with blazing light; he treated them with acid; and he fed them with strange diets, hoping in some such way to produce a mutation—a fruit fly that was different from the common run of its fellows. Nothing particularly interesting happened.

Then, in April, 1910, "in a pedigreed culture of *Drosophila* which had been running for nearly a year through a considerable number of generations, a male appeared with white eyes." This was extraordinary, for all the other thousands of fruit flies in Morgan's bottles had red eyes. Here was a mutation that he could use for his experiment.

Morgan was greatly excited at this discovery. It appeared to him now that all his long months of experiment, all his patient and meticulous work, were finally bringing him results. Breeding this white-eyed male with a red-eyed female, he succeeded after a few generations in establishing a pure-breeding race of white-eyed flies.

As time passed, Morgan and his assistants, examining the fruit flies under their microscopes, found twenty-five distinct mutations—fruit flies with crooked wings, with speckled wings, with variations in color, without eyes. They interbred and crossbred carefully.

Very soon Morgan had some new facts on heredity. The factors that bear the various inherited characters are like little disks strung on the thread of the chromosome, he said. He guessed there might be as many as ten thousand little disks, which he called *genes,* in some chromosomes.

When the egg is fertilized by the sperm the slender threads of the chromosomes twist around one another in what is called the "chromosomal embrace." Then some of the genes from one side pass over to the other side. Some of them might be knocked off or brushed aside and lost—this would be sufficient cause for mutation.

But it is the combination of genes that determines the character of the new individual, an organism that is new, for it bears a new combination of genes, yet old, for it is composed of the same material that has been passed down from generation to generation.

For several years Morgan and his assistants worked over their fruit flies, recording their pedigrees and examining them for mutations, observing how some genes were linked so that certain types appeared only in the males and others only in the females. Then they realized that the genes appeared in a regular order in the chromosomes. The gene for red eyes always occurred at the top of the chromosome, while that for speckled wings would be near the bottom. Gradually they succeeded in locating hundreds of genes and so made a series of chromosome diagrams.

How Mendel would have enjoyed seeing those fruit-fly experiments! How De Vries would have marveled at the gene maps!

But what is the practical importance of work like Morgan's? Will it help us to produce richer grain fields, heavier fruit, sturdier cattle? Will it help to produce a more intelligent or wiser race of men, or a healthier one? Not yet, at any rate. Grain, fruit, and cattle are being improved by selective breeding, but not with the help of gene maps. Very little indeed is definitely known about human heredity.

This does not mean that the present studies in heredity will never be of practical use. For whatever leads to a clearer understanding of nature's ways will be useful.

Three hundred years ago William Harvey announced that he had watched the circulation of blood in the human body, and so encouraged men to set aside their old notions and investigate the functions of the body's organs. In the same way biologists who study the arrangement of the genes in various species are just at the beginning of a new study.

Great though it is, the work of the modern biologists must be considered with humility. There are so many things in the living world that cannot yet be explained.

All forms of matter on the earth, organic and inorganic, are made up of atoms of different elements, we say. All living things have developed through a long process of evolution. We know something about them. We know something about laws of heredity.

But we still do not understand the process by which a green leaf manufactures food. Nor do we know exactly why a migrant bird sets off on its long journey. Neither can we understand why animals and men can remember what is past or why men are able to plan for the future.

We have not come to the end of understanding. We are still at the beginning.

INDEX

INDEX

Academy of Sciences, French, 64, 110, 146

Academy, The, in Athens, 22, 23, 24

Acquired characteristics, theory of, 116-17; giraffe as example of, 116

Adam's rib, 54

Albertus Magnus, 47

Alexander the Great, 23, 24, 27

Alexandria, Museum of, 65

Amoebas, 151

Anatomical Institute, Berlin, 142, 143

Angler (fish), Aristotle's description of, 20, 21

Antelopes, Minoan paintings of, 16

Ant-lion, description of in *Physiologus*, 45

Aphids, reproduction of, 82

Aristotle, 17-27, 47, 133, 174; studies catfish and other marine life, 19-21; studies mammals, 22; collects first library, 23; establishes zoological garden, 23; founds Lyceum, 24; arranges *scala natura*, 25, 26; studies embryos, 26; place in science of, 26, 27; death of, 27; writings, 33, 46, 59

Articulates, classified by Cuvier, 103

Auricle, studied by Harvey, 57

Bacon, Francis, 60-62, 173; *Novum Organum*, 61; conception of scientific truth, 61

Bacon, Roger, 47

Bacteriology, Pasteur pioneers in, 82

Baer, Karl Ernst von, 132-40, 141, 147; finds egg of mammal, 135-136; with Pander works out theory of germ layers, 136-37; collects embryos, 137-38; studies changes in embryos, 138-39; refuses to accept evolution, 138

Beagle, voyage of, 123-25

Bees, Swammerdam's study of, 76-77

Bible of Nature, The (Swammerdam), 77

Binomial nomenclature, of Linnaeus, 93

Blood, circulation of, *see* Harvey

Boerhaave, Hermann, 77-78, 91

Botanic Garden, of University of Uppsala, 94

Botticelli, 50

Boyle, Robert, 65

Brown, Robert, 126, 152

Brünn Society for Study of Natural Science, 163, 164

Buffon, Georges de, 100, 101, 110

Calcar, Jan Stephen von, 52

Calvert, Frederick, Lord Baltimore, 95

Capillary system, not understood by Harvey, 59; observed by Malpighi, 71-72

Carlyle, Thomas, 126

Catastrophes, theory of, *see* Cuvier

Catfish, Aristotle studies, 19

Catherine, Empress of Russia, 94

Cell, theory of, 146-47; controversy over theory, 147-48; description of, 148; definition of, by Schultze, 149; structure of, 153; movement in, 156